# Mathematics with Unifix® Cubes

## Hands-On Activities for the Standards

### Grade 1

Didax

Order Number 211090
ISBN 978-1-58324-323-7

B C D E F 15 14 13 12 11

395 Main Street
Rowley, MA 01969
www.didax.com

# CONTENTS

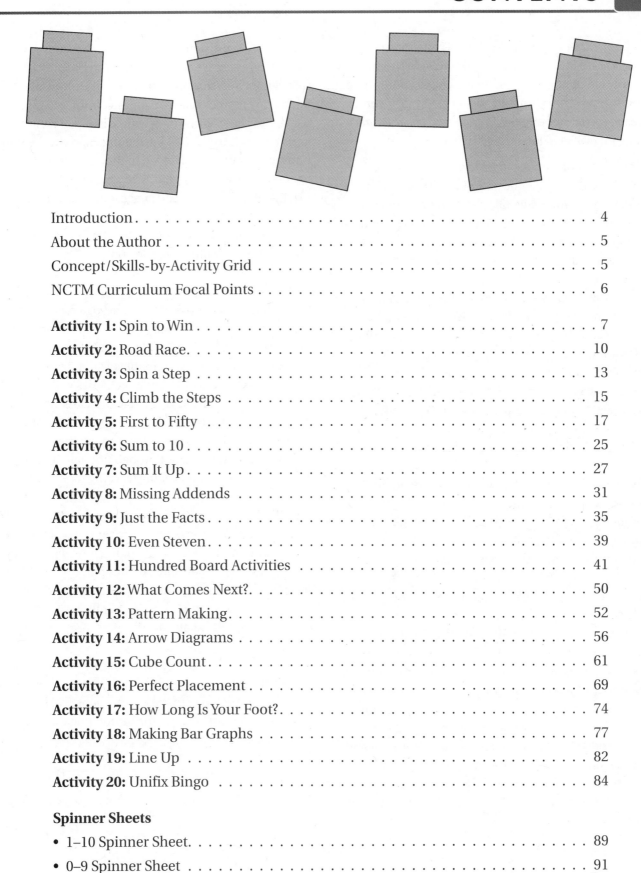

# INTRODUCTION

*Mathematics with Unifix Cubes* is organized around basic mathematical concepts taught in the early elementary grades. Relevant focal points and related connections from the recent National Council of Teachers of Mathematics *Curriculum Focal Points* (2006) are provided for each activity.

Since their appearance more than 50 years ago, Unifix Cubes have become part of mathematics education throughout the world. The structured quality, bright colors, and durability of Unifix Cubes provide an exciting appeal for young children during early mathematical learning. They present a positive basis for the exploration and expansion of early mathematics. The principal value of Unifix Cubes lies in their capacity to present students with easily structured, concrete analogues of concepts involving numbers and operations. With minimal additional work on the part of teachers, geometry, measurement, algebra, and probability/statistics ideas can also be explored. All of these areas have taken on added importance in today's mathematics curriculum. Successful learning of mathematics is enhanced when Unifix Cubes are used.

- Students develop confidence and independent thinking in mathematics.
- Students have time to explore new interests and to think about mathematics.
- Students communicate about mathematics.

As students begin learning mathematics, it is important to note the value that mathematics educators have placed on the use of manipulatives at all grade levels. Research has shown that students learn and understand mathematics better when they are able to manipulate objects or construct models. The need for concrete materials such as Unifix Cubes is not limited to children in preschool or in the primary grades but is also needed for many students in middle school and high school. The ancient proverb "I hear, I forget; I see, I remember; I do, I understand," is indeed a statement that rings true for today's students in the study of mathematics.

The games and activities in this book focus on the student as an active participant in the learning process through the physical manipulation of Unifix Cubes. Each one provides ready-made sheets for teachers to use in the classroom, along with a listing of concepts and skills, related NCTM focal points and connections, number of students involved in the activity, materials needed, directions for getting ready to use the activity, directions for play, and suggestions for variations in play. Some duplicating, cutting, and coloring are needed for various activities; however, most of the materials are contained in the book.

The Unifix Cube games and activities presented in these grade-level books are not part of a rigid curriculum, nor are they related to any prescriptive program. The cubes themselves provide a highly flexible and adaptable manipulative, capable of supporting cognitive and heuristic mathematics activities with meaning and self-evident proof. From Piagetian tasks such as conservation of quantity and one-to-one correspondence to basic operations, simple measurement, graphing, and ideas about probability, activities with the cubes become an exciting learning tool.

Unifix Cubes are unit-based as compared to base-10 blocks. Therefore, the activities cover a wide range of early mathematics. Although color has no significance as a representation of value, it does play an important role when dealing with various patterning activities. In turn, these activities provide an important link to algebraic thinking at an early level.

A student's excitement in learning and understanding mathematics is a joy for all teachers. It is hoped that the games and activities in this book will help provide a solid foundation for stimulating that learning excitement.

— Don S. Balka

## About the Author

**Don S. Balka, Ph.D.,** is a noted mathematics educator who has presented more than 2,000 workshops on the use of math manipulatives with elementary school-aged children at national and regional conferences of the National Council of Teachers of Mathematics and at in-service trainings in school districts throughout the United States. He has visited and taught classes in schools throughout the United Kingdom and Ireland, where Unifix materials are an integral part of the mathematics classroom.

Balka is the author or co-author of numerous books for K–8 teachers, including *Developing Algebraic Thinking with Number Tiles, Hands-On Math and Literature with Math-Start, Exploring Geometry with Geofix,* and *2D and 3D Geometry with Interlocking Shapes.*

Balka has served as director of the National Council of Teachers of Mathematics, the National Council of Supervisors of Mathematics, and TODOS: Mathematics for All. He also served on the board of the School Science and Mathematics Association and is now president-elect.

## Concept/Skills-by-Activity Grid

| CONCEPT/SKILL | 1 | 2 | 3 | 4 | 5 | 6 | 7 | 8 | 9 | 10 | 11 | 12 | 13 | 14 | 15 | 16 | 17 | 18 | 19 | 20 |
|---|---|---|---|---|---|---|---|---|---|---|---|---|---|---|---|---|---|---|---|---|
| Counting | X | X |  | X |  |  |  | X |  |  | X |  |  |  | X |  |  |  |  |  |
| Greater than/less than | X |  |  | X |  |  |  | X |  |  | X |  |  |  | X |  |  |  |  |  |
| One-to-one correspondence |  | X | X |  |  |  |  |  |  |  | X |  |  |  |  |  |  |  |  |  |
| Addition |  | X |  | X |  | X | X | X | X |  |  |  |  |  |  |  |  |  |  |  |
| Subtraction |  | X |  |  |  |  |  | X | X |  |  |  |  |  |  |  |  |  |  |  |
| Number recognition |  |  |  |  | X |  |  |  |  |  | X |  |  |  |  |  |  |  |  | X |
| Number words |  |  |  |  | X |  |  |  |  |  | X |  |  |  |  |  |  |  |  |  |
| Counting on |  |  |  |  | X |  |  |  |  |  |  |  |  |  |  |  |  |  |  |  |
| Even and odd numbers |  |  |  |  |  |  |  |  |  | X | X |  |  |  |  |  |  |  |  |  |
| One more than/one less than |  | X |  |  |  |  |  |  |  |  | X |  |  |  |  |  |  |  |  |  |
| Place value |  |  |  |  |  |  |  |  |  |  | X |  |  | X |  |  |  |  |  |  |
| Color recognition |  |  |  |  |  |  |  |  |  |  |  | X | X |  |  |  |  |  |  | X |
| Patterning |  |  |  |  |  |  |  |  |  |  |  | X | X |  |  |  |  |  |  |  |
| Algebraic reasoning |  |  |  |  |  |  |  |  |  |  |  |  |  | X |  |  |  |  |  |  |
| Ordered pairs |  |  |  |  |  |  |  |  |  |  |  |  |  | X |  |  |  |  |  |  |
| Graphing |  |  |  |  |  |  |  |  |  |  |  |  |  | X |  |  | X | X |  |  |
| Perimeter/area |  |  |  |  |  |  |  |  |  |  |  |  | X |  |  |  |  |  |  |  |
| Spatial reasoning |  |  |  |  |  |  |  |  |  |  |  |  |  | X |  |  |  |  |  |  |
| Spatial terms |  |  |  |  |  |  |  |  |  |  |  |  |  | X |  |  |  |  |  |  |
| Estimating length |  |  |  |  |  |  |  |  |  |  |  |  |  |  |  |  | X |  |  |  |
| Measuring length |  |  |  |  |  |  |  |  |  |  |  |  |  |  |  |  | X |  |  |  |
| Ordering by length |  |  |  |  |  |  |  |  |  |  |  |  |  |  |  |  |  |  | X |  |

| | Connections to the Focal Points | | | Grade 1 Curriculum Focal Points | | | |
|---|---|---|---|---|---|---|---|
| **Algebra:** Through identifying, describing, and applying number patterns and properties in developing strategies for basic facts, children learn about other properties of numbers and operations, such as odd and even, and 0 as the identity element for addition. | **Measurement and Data Analysis:** Children strengthen their sense of number by solving problems involving measurements and data. | **Number and Operations and Algebra:** Children use mathematical reasoning, including ideas such as commutativity and associativity and beginning ideas of tens and ones, to solve two-digit addition and subtraction problems with strategies that they understand and can explain. They solve both routine and nonroutine problems. | **Geometry:** Composing and decomposing geometric shapes | **Number and Operations:** Developing an understanding of whole number relationships, including grouping in tens and ones | **Number and Operations and Algebra:** Developing understandings of addition and subtraction and strategies for basic addition facts and related subtraction facts | Activity |
| | | | | | X | Spin to Win, pp. 7–9 |
| | | | | | X | Road Race, pp. 10–12 |
| | | | | X | X | Spin a Step, pp. 13–14 |
| | | X | | | X | Climb the Steps, pp. 15–16 |
| | | | | X | X | First to Fifty, pp. 17–24 |
| | | X | | | X | Sum to 10, pp. 25–26 |
| | | X | | | X | Sum It Up, pp. 27–30 |
| | | X | | | X | Missing Addends, pp. 31–34 |
| | | X | | | X | Just the Facts, pp. 35–38 |
| | | | | | | Even Steven, pp. 39–40 |
| | | X | | X | X | Hundred Board Activities, pp. 41–49 |
| X | | | | | | What Comes Next? pp. 50–51 |
| X | | | | | X | Pattern Making, pp. 52–55 |
| X | | | X | X | X | Arrow Diagrams, pp. 56–60 |
| | X | | X | | | Cube Count, pp. 61–68 |
| | | | X | | | Perfect Placement, pp. 69–73 |
| | X | | | | | How Long Is Your Foot? pp. 74–76 |
| | X | | | | | Making Bar Graphs, pp. 77–81 |
| | X | | | | | Line Up, pp. 82–83 |
| | X | | | | | Unifix Bingo, pp. 84–85 |

# SPIN TO WIN

## Concept or Skills

Counting, greater than/less than (more/less)

## NCTM Curriculum Focal Point

**Number and Operations and Algebra:** Addition and subtraction strategies

## Number of Students

2

## Materials

For each student:

- 10 Unifix Cubes of the same color

For each pair of students:

- Spin-to-Win Game Sheet
- More/Less Spinner Sheet
- Set of 10 markers (buttons, chips, rings)

## 🚩 Getting Ready

Make copies of the Spin-to-Win Game Sheet and More/Less Spinner Sheet for each pair of students.

Distribute 10 markers to each pair to use as "winner" awards for each round.

Initially, a teacher should demonstrate play to the entire class or pair of students, with each student grabbing a handful of Unifix Cubes.

## 🔧 Digging In

One side of the Spin-to-Win Game Sheet should be designated for each player.

In each round, players grab some or all of their 10 Unifix Cubes and place them on their side of the game sheet.

One player then spins the spinner on the More/Less Spinner Sheet.

If the arrow points to MORE, the player who has more Unifix Cubes wins the round and receives one marker as an award for the round. If the arrow points to LESS, the player who has fewer Unifix Cubes wins the round. If each player grabs the same number of cubes, either both receive a marker or neither receives a marker. Decide how to handle this situation before students play.

Instruct students to play five (or some designated number) of rounds. The player with more award markers at the end is the winner.

After each round, players should replace the Unifix Cubes drawn.

## ➡️ Going Further

Understanding vocabulary is critical at this age. The phrase "grab *some* of the cubes" is often taken to mean "grab *all* of the cubes." Spend some time discussing the distinction between the two words.

If students have difficulty in determining the winner of a round, have them connect the Unifix Cubes into bars and compare by length.

SPIN TO WIN

MORE/LESS SPINNER

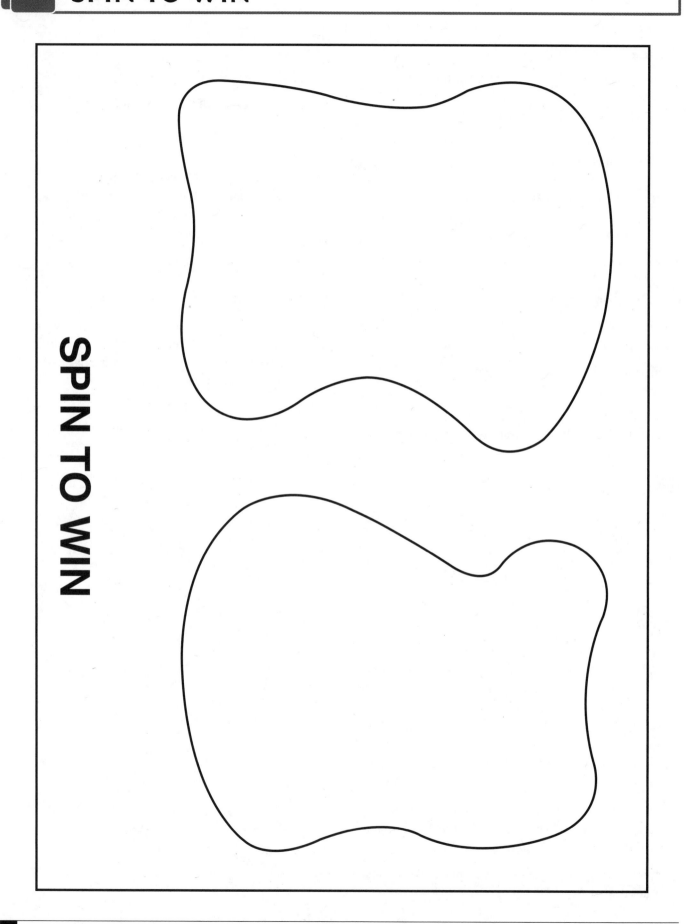

SPIN TO WIN

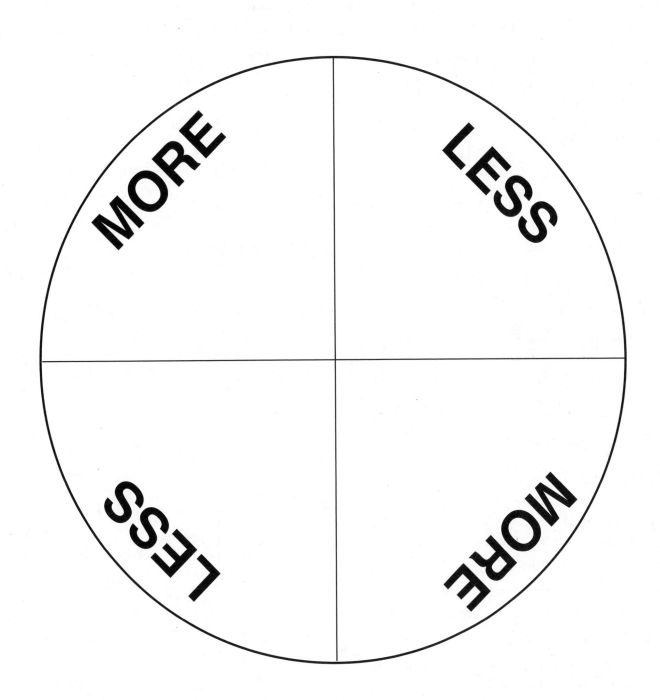

# MORE/LESS SPINNER

# ROAD RACE

## Concept or Skills

One-to-one correspondence between set and numeral, counting, beginning addition and subtraction

## NCTM Curriculum Focal Point

**Number and Operations and Algebra:** Addition and subtraction strategies

## Number of Students

2–4

## Materials

For each student:

- 20, 30, or 40 Unifix Cubes of the same color
- Road Race Track to 20, 30, or 40
- Several index cards (optional)

For each group:

- 1 regular six-sided die

---

## 🏁 Getting Ready

Make copies of the Road Race Track page. Cut apart the sections and tape or glue them together to make a continuous race track.

Depending on the level of addition and subtraction activities currently being done in class, use two or three sections of the Road Race Tracks for each student.

Distribute 20–40 Unifix Cubes of one color and several index cards (or sheets of paper) to each student. Each group gets a regular six-sided die.

## 🔧 Digging In

Taking turns, players toss the die, pick up the corresponding number of Unifix Cubes of one color, and place them on the Road Race Track.

The first player to exactly cover his or her track is the winner of the round.

Play five rounds to determine the winner of a race.

Players lose a turn if they go over 20 (or 30 or 40).

Have each player say aloud the total number of Unifix Cubes on the track after each turn and how many more Unifix Cubes are needed to win.

Then have the player write on an index card the corresponding number sentence (for example, 12 + 4 = 16).

## ➡️ Going Further

Reverse the procedures for Road Race. Players first fill the track with Unifix Cubes. Taking turns, players then toss the die and remove the corresponding number of Unifix Cubes from the track. The first player to exactly uncover his or her track is the winner of the round. Have each player write the corresponding subtraction number sentence on a card (for example, 18 − 6 = 12, 5 − 2 = 3).

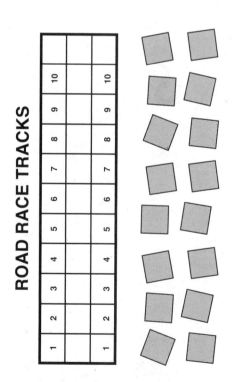

ROAD RACE TRACKS

Mathematics with Unifix® Cubes          © Didax, Inc. – www.didax.com

# ROAD RACE TRACKS

| 1 | | 1 |
|---|---|---|
| 2 | | 2 |
| 3 | | 3 |
| 4 | | 4 |
| 5 | | 5 |
| 6 | | 6 |
| 7 | | 7 |
| 8 | | 8 |
| 9 | | 9 |
| 10 | | 10 |
| | | |

| 11 | | 11 |
|---|---|---|
| 12 | | 12 |
| 13 | | 13 |
| 14 | | 14 |
| 15 | | 15 |
| 16 | | 16 |
| 17 | | 17 |
| 18 | | 18 |
| 19 | | 19 |
| 20 | | 20 |
| | | |

# ROAD RACE TRACKS

| | | |
|---|---|---|
| 21 | 22 | |
| 23 | 24 | 25 |
| 26 | 27 | 28 |
| 29 | 30 | |

| | | |
|---|---|---|
| 21 | 22 | |
| 23 | 24 | 25 |
| 26 | 27 | 28 |
| 29 | 30 | |

| | | |
|---|---|---|
| 31 | 32 | 33 |
| 34 | 35 | 36 |
| 37 | 38 | 39 |
| 40 | | |

| | | |
|---|---|---|
| 31 | 32 | 33 |
| 34 | 35 | 36 |
| 37 | 38 | 39 |
| 40 | | |

Mathematics with Unifix® Cubes

## Concept or Skills

One-to-one correspondence between set and numeral, one more than, one less than

## NCTM Curriculum Focal Point

**Number and Operations and Algebra:** Addition and subtraction strategies

## Number of Students

2–4

## Materials

For each student:

- 55 Unifix Cubes
- Unifix 1–10 Stair

For each group:

- 1–10 Spinner Sheet and spinner, or 0–9 Spinner Sheet, or 2–11 Spinner Sheet (pages 89–93)

## 1 Getting Ready

Distribute 55 Unifix Cubes and a Unifix 1–10 Stair to each student. For some students, the cubes need to be separated by number and color. For example: 1 red, 2 white, 3 light blue, 4 green, 5 yellow, 6 dark blue, 7 black, 8 maroon, 9 orange, 10 brown.

Each group of students needs a 1–10 Spinner Sheet and spinner.

## Digging In

Taking turns, the players spin the spinner, find the number of Unifix Cubes, and fill the corresponding step of the Stair on their activity sheet. For example, Player A spins a 4, finds four Unifix Cubes, and places them on the 4 step of his/her Stair.

If a step has already been filled, the player loses that turn.

The first player to completely fill his or her Stair is the winner.

## Going Further

Use a 0–9 Spinner Sheet. The directions are the same, except the player fills the step corresponding to "one more than" the number on the Spinner Sheet.

Use a 2–11 Spinner Sheet. The directions are the same, except the player fills the step corresponding to "one less than" the number on the Spinner Sheet.

Change the rules so that a player may play if a number has already been covered and the number appears again on a spin. For example, if the 5 step is already filled and a player spins another 5, then he or she may place five cubes on any other step that is vacant. If the cubes are placed on the 7 step, then the player will need to spin a 2 to fill that step. Have students use Unifix Cubes of a different color to show the completed step. For this example, 5 + 2 = 7 yields a basic addition fact.

In a similar way, if the 5 step is already filled and a player spins another 5, then the player may break (separate) the 5 into two parts (1 + 4, 2 + 3) and fill the appropriate steps with cubes.

The first player to completely fill his or her Stair is the winner.

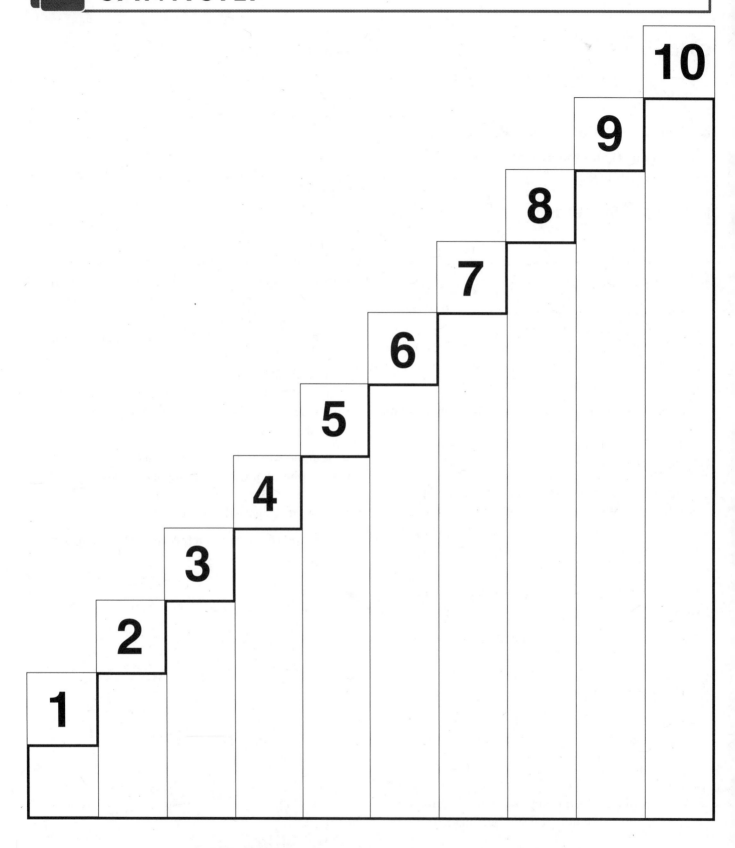

# UNIFIX 1–10 STAIR

Mathematics with Unifix® Cubes          © Didax, Inc. – www.didax.com

## Concept or Skills

Counting, basic addition facts, greater than/less than

## NCTM Curriculum Focal Point

**Number and Operations and Algebra:** Addition and subtraction strategies

## Number of Students

2

## Materials

For each student:

• 30 Unifix Cubes of one color

For each pair:

• Unifix 1–10 Stair
• 1–10 Spinner Sheet and spinner (page 89)
• 0–9 Spinner Sheet (optional) (page 91)

## Getting Ready

Make a copy of the Unifix 1–10 Stair for each pair of students.

Give each student 30 Unifix Cubes of one color.

Give each pair a 1–10 Spinner Sheet and spinner.

## Digging In

Player 1 spins the spinner and puts the corresponding number of Unifix Cubes in a bar. The player then places the bar in any open column of the Unifix 1–10 Stair.

Player 2 continues in a similar manner, either attaching his or her Unifix Cubes to those of Player 1 to fill a column or starting a new column.

If a step has already been filled or it is impossible to add Unifix Cubes to another column, then the player loses that turn. Cubes may not be split among two or more columns.

Students continue in this manner until the Unifix 1–10 Stair is completely filled. At this point, players remove their Unifix Cubes from the sheet, form bars of 10 cubes each, and count them. The winner is the player with more cubes.

## Going Further

Use a 0–9 Spinner Sheet. The directions are the same, except a player loses a turn if 0 is spun.

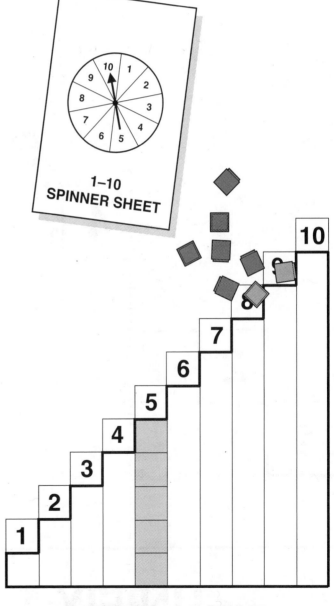

**UNIFIX 1–10 STAIR**

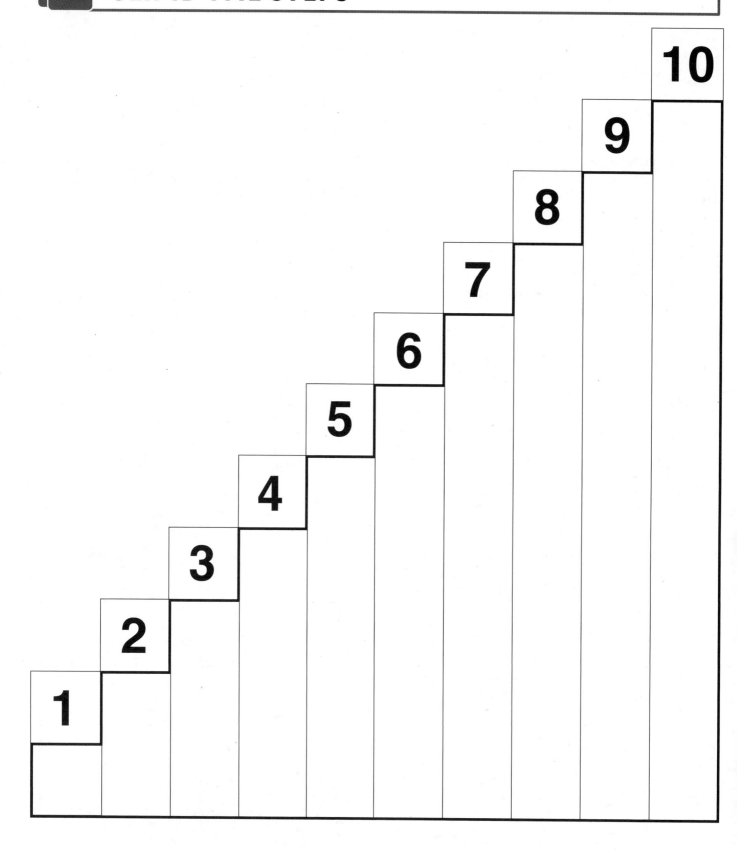

# UNIFIX 1–10 STAIR

Mathematics with Unifix® Cubes

## Concept or Skills

Numbers, number words, counting on

## NCTM Curriculum Focal Point

**Number and Operations and Algebra:** Addition and subtraction strategies

**Number and Operations:** Whole number relationships, including grouping of tens and ones

## Number of Students

2 or entire class

## Materials

For each student:

- 50 Unifix Cubes
- First-to-Fifty Mat

For each group:

- Number Cards
- Number Word Cards

## Getting Ready

Make a copy of the First-to-Fifty Mat for each student.

Make a copy of the Number Cards or the Number Word Cards and cut them apart.

If an overhead projector is used for an entire class, make transparencies of the Number or Number Word Cards and cut them apart.

Distribute 50 Unifix Cubes to each student.

## Digging In

If teaching a group of two, show a Number or Number Word Card to the pair of students. Have the students place the corresponding number of Unifix Cubes on the First-to-Fifty Mat. Say:

> **Here is a number (or number word). Cover the same number of squares on your mat with Unifix Cubes.**

Allow time for students to complete the task.

Repeat the task until the students have covered their entire First-to-Fifty Mat.

If a final Number or Number Word Card makes more than 50, discuss how many more than 50.

## Going Further

When students understand the activity, have pairs of students play as a game.

Taking turns, the players draw a Number (or Number Word) Card and covers the corresponding number of squares with Unifix Cubes. The first player to completely cover his or her First-to-Fifty Mat is the winner.

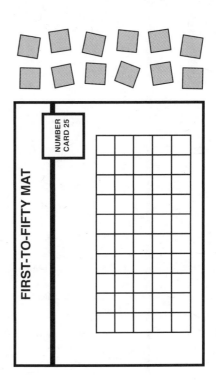

FIRST-TO-FIFTY MAT

NUMBER CARD 25

# FIRST-TO-FIFTY MAT

Mathematics with Unifix® Cubes © Didax, Inc. – www.didax.com

## NUMBER CARDS

| | | | |
|---|---|---|---|
| 1 | 2 | 3 | 4 |
| 5 | 6 | 7 | 8 |
| 9 | 10 | 11 | 12 |
| 13 | 14 | 15 | 16 |
| 17 | 18 | 19 | 20 |

## NUMBER CARDS

| | | | |
|---|---|---|---|
| 21 | 22 | 23 | 24 |
| 25 | 26 | 27 | 28 |
| 29 | 30 | 31 | 32 |
| 33 | 34 | 35 | 36 |
| 37 | 38 | 39 | 40 |

Mathematics with Unifix® Cubes

## NUMBER CARDS

| | | | |
|---|---|---|---|
| 41 | 42 | 43 | 44 |
| 45 | 46 | 47 | 48 |
| 49 | 50 | | |
| | | | |
| | | | |

# NUMBER WORD CARDS

| | | | |
|---|---|---|---|
| one | two | three | four |
| five | six | seven | eight |
| nine | ten | eleven | twelve |
| thirteen | fourteen | fifteen | sixteen |
| seventeen | eighteen | nineteen | twenty |

# NUMBER WORD CARDS

| | | | |
|---|---|---|---|
| twenty-one | twenty-two | twenty-three | twenty-four |
| twenty-five | twenty-six | twenty-seven | twenty-eight |
| twenty-nine | thirty | thirty-one | thirty-two |
| thirty-three | thirty-four | thirty-five | thirty-six |
| thirty-seven | thirty-eight | thirty-nine | forty |

# NUMBER WORD CARDS

| | | | |
|---|---|---|---|
| forty-one | forty-two | forty-three | forty-four |
| forty-five | forty-six | forty-seven | forty-eight |
| forty-nine | fifty | | |
| | | | |
| | | | |

## Concept or Skills

Basic addition facts for sums to 10

## NCTM Curriculum Focal Point

**Number and Operations and Algebra:** Addition and subtraction strategies

## Number of Students

Small groups

## Materials

For each student:

- 55 Unifix Cubes
- Sum-to-10 Game Sheet

For each group:

- 0–9 Spinner Sheet and spinner (page 91)
- 1–10 Spinner (optional) (page 89)
- 2–11 Spinner (optional) (page 93)

## Getting Ready

Distribute 55 Unifix Cubes and a Sum-to-10 Game Sheet to each student. Each group gets a 0–9 Spinner Sheet and spinner.

## Digging In

Taking turns, each player spins the spinner, finds the number of Unifix Cubes, and fills the appropriate column of the game sheet so that the sum is 10. For example, if a player spins a 4, he or she finds four Unifix Cubes and places them in the 6 column of the sheet, since 6 + 4 = 10. Each player says aloud and writes the corresponding number sentence.

If a column has already been filled, the player loses that turn.

The first player to complete all 10 number sentences is the winner.

## Going Further

Use the 1–10 Spinner Sheet and spinner. Instruct players to fill the columns of the game sheet with Unifix Cubes. Taking turns, players spin the spinner and remove the corresponding number of Unifix Cubes from the game sheet. The player states and writes the corresponding subtraction number sentence—for example, 10 – 4 = 6 or 10 – 1 = 9. If a column has already been uncovered, then the player loses that turn. The first player to complete all 10 subtraction number sentences is the winner.

Use the 0–9 Spinner Sheet. For early number work, the player fills the column corresponding to "one more than" the number on the Spinner Sheet.

Use the 2–11 Spinner Sheet. For early number work, the player fills the column corresponding to "one less than" the number on the Spinner Sheet.

Change the rules so that a player may play if a number has already been covered and the number appears again on a spin. For example, if the 5 column is already filled and the player spins another 5, he or she may place five cubes in any other column that is vacant. If the cubes are placed in the 7 column the player must spin a 2 to complete the column. Have students use two different colors of Unifix Cubes to show the basic addition fact represented by the filled column—for example, 5 + 2 = 7.

Alternatively, if the 5 column is already filled and the player spins another 5, he or she may break the 5 into two parts (1 + 4 or 2 + 3) and fill the appropriate columns with cubes.

The first player to completely fill his or her game sheet is the winner.

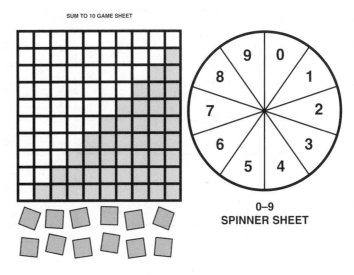

SUM TO 10 GAME SHEET

0–9
SPINNER SHEET

# SUM TO 10 GAME SHEET

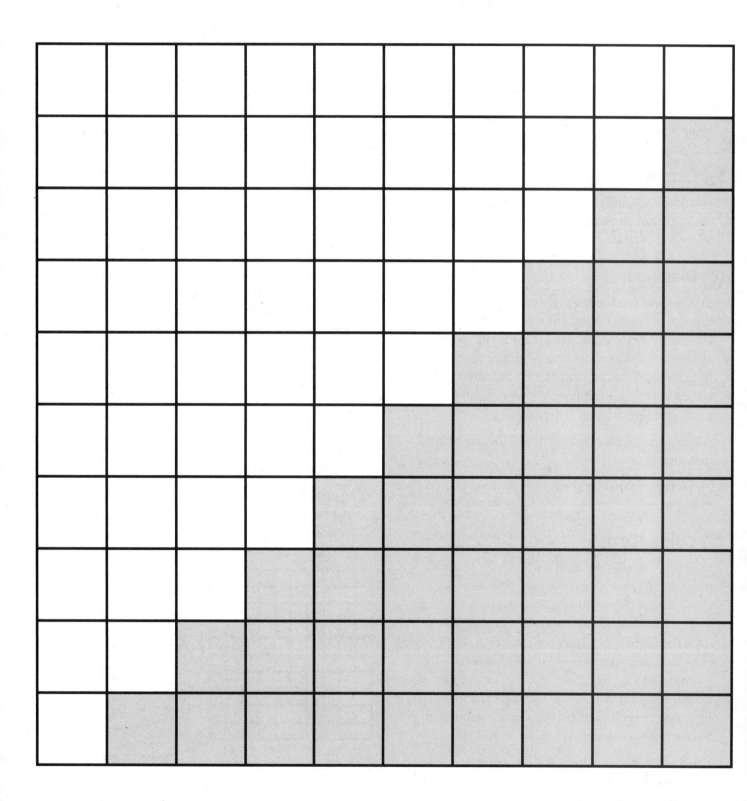

Mathematics with Unifix® Cubes
© Didax, Inc. – www.didax.com

## Concept or Skills

Basic addition facts to a sum of 10, commutative property for addition

## NCTM Curriculum Focal Point

**Number and Operations and Algebra:** Addition and subtraction strategies

## Number of Students

1 or a small group

## Materials

For each student:

- 20 Unifix Cubes of one color and 20 of a different color
- Number Sentence Grids for Sums 2–5, 6–10, and blank
- 0–9 Spinner Sheet and spinner (optional) (page 91)

---

## 🕐 Getting Ready

Make copies of the appropriate Number Sentence Grids for each student. Distribute the grids and the Unifix Cubes to the students.

## 🔧 Digging In

There are ten basic addition facts up to a sum of 5, excluding those involving 0 as an addend:

1 + 1, 1 + 2, 1 + 3, 1 + 4, 2 + 1, 2 + 2, 2 + 3, 3 + 1, 3 + 2, 4 + 1

Have students place Unifix Cubes on the Number Sentence Grid, using cubes in two different colors. Students find the sum by counting the number of cubes and then write the number sentence illustrated by the cubes, as shown below.

**NUMBER SENTENCE GRIDS (SUMS 2–5)**

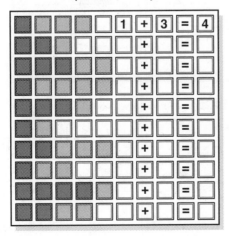

Ask questions such as:

> How many ways are there to get a sum of 2? 3? 4? 5?

> If 0 were an addend, how many ways would there be to get a sum of 2? 3? 4? 5?

## ➡️ Going Further

For students working on basic facts greater than 5, use the Number Sentence Grid for Sums 6–10 or construct your own grids. Students place Unifix Cubes on the grids and find the sum as before. Following is an example of a grid sheet.

In a game format with a small group, each player gets a Number Sentence Grid and 40 or more Unifix Cubes (20 of each color). Each group gets a 0–9 Spinner Sheet and spinner.

Taking turns, players spin the spinner and cover all squares where the number spun is an addend. A player who spins a number (addend) that has already been covered loses that turn. A player who spins a 0 loses that turn. As players complete a row, they write the number sentence in the row below it. The winner is the first player to correctly complete the number sentences on his or her grid.

# NUMBER SENTENCE GRIDS
## (SUMS 2–5)

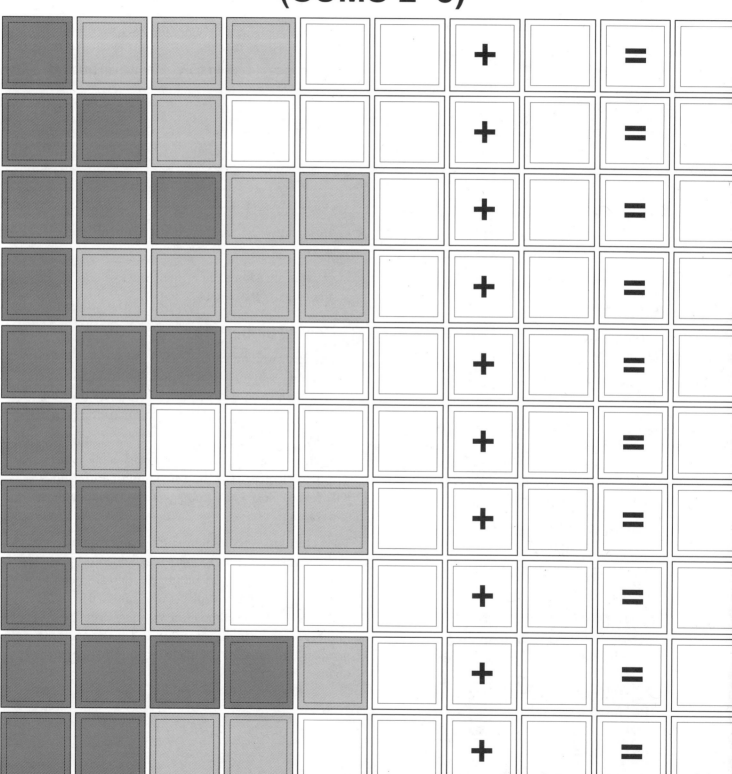

Mathematics with Unifix® Cubes     © Didax, Inc. – www.didax.com

# NUMBER SENTENCE GRIDS
## (SUMS 6–10)

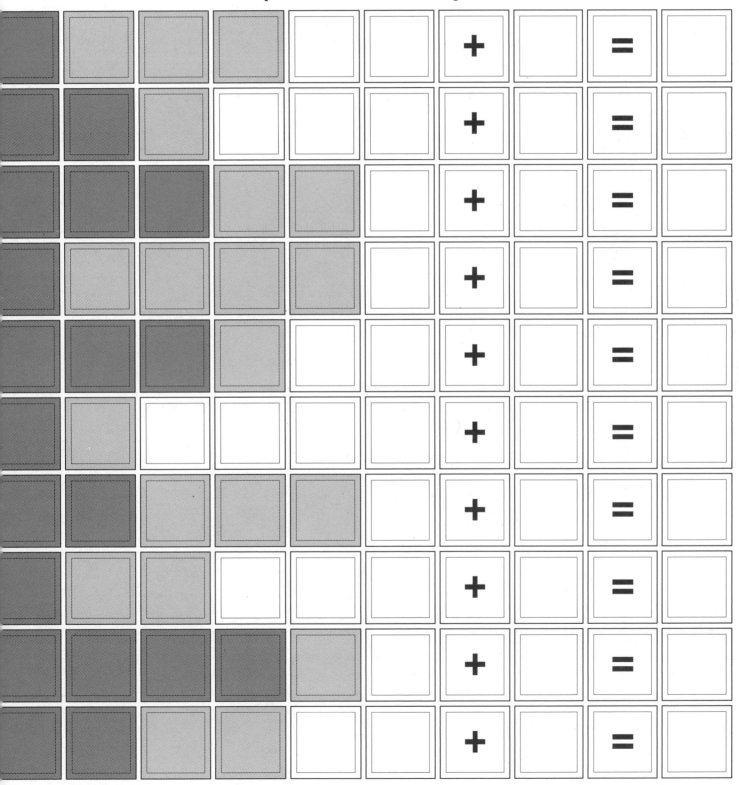

# NUMBER SENTENCE GRIDS
## (Blank)

Mathematics with Unifix® Cubes

© Didax, Inc. – www.didax.com

## Concept or Skills

Counting, basic addition and subtraction facts, greater than/less than

## NCTM Curriculum Focal Point

**Number and Operations and Algebra:** Addition and subtraction strategies

## Number of Students

2

## Materials:

For each student:

- 55 Unifix Cubes of one color
- Unifix 1–10 Stair

For each pair of students:

- Missing Addend cards
- 0–9 Spinner Sheet (page 91) and spinner

---

## 🔷 Getting Ready

Make a copy of the Unifix 1–10 Stair for each student or pair of students.

Make a copy of the Missing Addend Cards for each pair of students and cut them apart.

Give 55 Unifix Cubes of one color to each student. (The two students get different colors.)

Give a 0–9 Spinner Sheet and spinner to each group.

## 🔶 Digging In

### Activity 1

Give each student a Missing Addend Card and a 1–10 Stair. The students place Unifix Cubes on the steps corresponding to the known addends on the card. For example, for 3 + ___ = 7, the student places 3 Unifix Cubes on the 7 step.

Then students exchange their 1–10 Stairs and complete filling the steps with Unifix Cubes. Each student should then write the missing addends on their card.

### Activity 2

Give each player a Missing Addend Card and 1–10 Stair. The players place Unifix Cubes on their 1–10 Stair corresponding to the known addends on their card.

Taking turns, players spin the spinner and put the corresponding number of Unifix Cubes in a bar. The players then place the bar on a step so that the step is completely filled. If it is impossible to use this "missing addend," the player loses that turn.

The first player to completely fill the five steps corresponding to the addends on the card is the winner.

## ➡ Going Further

Distribute a 1–10 Stair and 55 Unifix Cubes to each student.

Have students cover the steps on their 1–10 Stair with the cubes.

Give each student a Missing Addend Card. Have the students remove the known addend from the step corresponding to the indicated sum to find the missing addend. For example, if the problem is 3 + ___ = 7, the student would remove three Unifix Cubes from the 7 step, leaving a "missing addend" of 4.

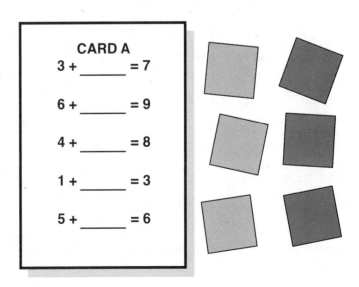

**CARD A**

3 + _____ = 7

6 + _____ = 9

4 + _____ = 8

1 + _____ = 3

5 + _____ = 6

---

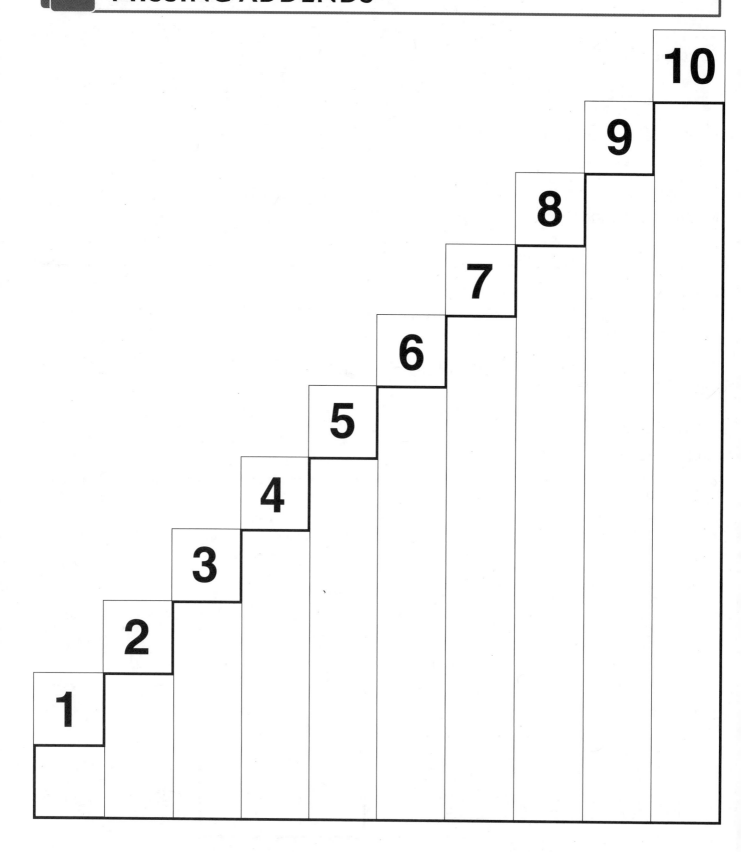

# UNIFIX 1–10 STAIR

# MISSING ADDEND CARDS

**CARD A**

3 + _____ = 7

6 + _____ = 9

4 + _____ = 8

1 + _____ = 3

5 + _____ = 6

**CARD B**

2 + _____ = 5

7 + _____ = 10

4 + _____ = 6

1 + _____ = 7

6 + _____ = 9

**CARD C**

3 + _____ = 8

5 + _____ = 10

7 + _____ = 9

1 + _____ = 6

2 + _____ = 7

**CARD D**

8 + _____ = 10

2 + _____ = 6

5 + _____ = 8

1 + _____ = 5

3 + _____ = 7

# MISSING ADDEND CARDS

### CARD E

$4 + \rule{2cm}{0.4pt} = 9$

$6 + \rule{2cm}{0.4pt} = 10$

$2 + \rule{2cm}{0.4pt} = 8$

$3 + \rule{2cm}{0.4pt} = 6$

$5 + \rule{2cm}{0.4pt} = 7$

### CARD F

$1 + \rule{2cm}{0.4pt} = 4$

$4 + \rule{2cm}{0.4pt} = 10$

$6 + \rule{2cm}{0.4pt} = 8$

$3 + \rule{2cm}{0.4pt} = 7$

$5 + \rule{2cm}{0.4pt} = 9$

### CARD G

$0 + \rule{2cm}{0.4pt} = 5$

$2 + \rule{2cm}{0.4pt} = 9$

$6 + \rule{2cm}{0.4pt} = 7$

$3 + \rule{2cm}{0.4pt} = 8$

$4 + \rule{2cm}{0.4pt} = 6$

### CARD H

$3 + \rule{2cm}{0.4pt} = 3$

$9 + \rule{2cm}{0.4pt} = 10$

$5 + \rule{2cm}{0.4pt} = 7$

$4 + \rule{2cm}{0.4pt} = 8$

$2 + \rule{2cm}{0.4pt} = 5$

## Concept or Skills

Beginning addition and subtraction using basic fact families

## NCTM Curriculum Focal Point

**Number and Operations and Algebra:** Addition and subtraction strategies

## Number of Students

1–2

## Materials

For each student:

• 18 Unifix Cubes of one color

For each group:

• Fact Family Number Cards

---

## 🔲 Getting Ready

Make copies of the Fact Family Number Cards and cut them apart. Note that the cards do not include 0 as an addend or sum.

Distribute 18 Unifix Cubes of one color to each student or pair of students.

## ⛏ Digging In

As an individual assessment activity, present a Fact Family Number Card to the student. Say:

> **I will show a Fact Family Number Card. With the Unifix Cubes, I want you to show me and tell me each member of the fact family.**

Allow time for the student to show each member of the fact family. For example, if the card shows 4, 6, 10, the members of the fact family are $4 + 6 = 10$, $6 + 4 = 10$, $10 - 4 = 6$, and $10 - 6 = 4$.

For some fact families there are only two family members, since the remaining two are identical. For example, consider 2, 2, and 4. The only members of the family are $2 + 2 = 4$ and $4 - 2 = 2$.

Repeat the task so that a student completes fact families for at least five number cards.

## ➡ Going Further

Show students how to complete the activity in pairs. Model one of the Fact Family Number Cards with the entire class. Give each pair of students 18 Unifix Cubes and four or six number cards.

One student selects a card and the other student models the members of the fact family with the Unifix Cubes. Students reverse roles and repeat the task until all cards have been used.

The following questions will help assess a student's responses to the tasks presented:

• Did the student correctly show each of the four (or two) members of a particular fact family?
• Did the student correctly state the members of a fact family?
• If the student experienced difficulty in showing the members of a fact family, was there an observable pattern in the errors?
• Were particular sets of numbers more difficult than others?

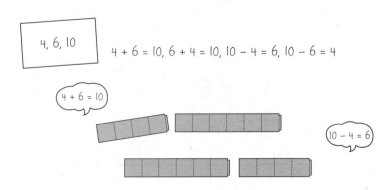

# FACT FAMILY NUMBER CARDS

| | | |
|---|---|---|
| 1, 1, 2 | 1, 6, 7 | 2, 3, 5 |
| 1, 2, 3 | 1, 7, 8 | 2, 4, 6 |
| 1, 3, 4 | 1, 8, 9 | 2, 5, 7 |
| 1, 4, 5 | 1, 9, 10 | 2, 6, 8 |
| 1, 5, 6 | 2, 2, 4 | 2, 7, 9 |

Mathematics with Unifix® Cubes

# FACT FAMILY NUMBER CARDS

| | | |
|---|---|---|
| 2, 8, 10 | 3, 6, 9 | 4, 5, 9 |
| 2, 9, 11 | 3, 7, 10 | 4, 6, 10 |
| 3, 3, 6 | 3, 8, 11 | 4, 7, 11 |
| 3, 4, 7 | 3, 9, 12 | 4, 8, 12 |
| 3, 5, 8 | 4, 4, 8 | 4, 9, 13 |

# FACT FAMILY NUMBER CARDS

| | | |
|---|---|---|
| 5, 5, 10 | 6, 6, 12 | 7, 8, 15 |
| 5, 6, 11 | 6, 7, 13 | 7, 9, 16 |
| 5, 7, 12 | 6, 8, 14 | 8, 8, 16 |
| 5, 8, 13 | 6, 9, 15 | 8, 9, 17 |
| 5, 9, 14 | 7, 7, 14 | 9, 9, 18 |

# EVEN STEVEN

## Concept or Skills

Even and odd numbers

## NCTM Curriculum Focal Point

**Algebra Connection:** Properties of numbers, such as odd and even

## Number of Students

2

## Materials

For each pair of students:

- 20 Unifix Cubes (10 for each student)
- Even Steven Activity Sheet
- 1–10 Spinner Sheet (page 89) and spinner

### 🚩 Getting Ready

Make a copy of the Even Steven Activity Sheet and 1–10 Spinner Sheet for each pair of students.

Distribute 10 Unifix Cubes to each student. Distribute a 1–10 Spinner Sheet, spinner, and activity sheet to each group.

### 🔧 Digging In

For this game, Unifix Cubes will be used as markers.

Designate one student to use the "even" path and the other to use the "odd" path.

The "even" player spins the spinner first. If the spinner lands on an even number, the player places a Unifix Cube on the first square on the even side of the activity sheet. If the spinner lands on an odd number, the player loses that turn.

The "odd" player then spins the spinner. If the spinner lands on an odd number, the player places a Unifix Cube on the first square on the odd side of the activity sheet. If the spinner lands on an even number, the player loses the turn.

The game continues in this manner until one player completely fills his or her side of the activity sheet.

### ➡️ Going Further

Instead of one player losing a turn, allow the other player to cover a square. For example, if the "even" player spins an odd number, the "odd" player gets to place a Unifix Cube on the "odd" path and then also take his or her turn.

Place 20 Unifix Cubes in a paper bag. Taking turns, students grab cubes from the bag and place them on the desk. For early work on even and odd numbers, students might place the cubes in two parallel rows. If there is a one-to-one correspondence, there is an even number of cubes; if one cube remains, there is an odd number of cubes.

Cubes are returned to the bag after each turn.

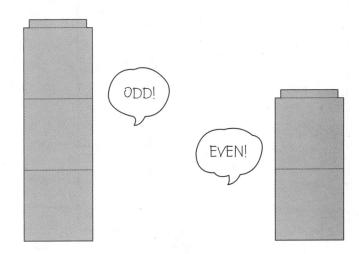

**EVEN**

START

END

**ODD**

START

END

Mathematics with Unifix® Cubes          © Didax, Inc. – www.didax.com

## Concept or Skills

One-to-one correspondence, number words and corresponding numbers, one more than/one less than, greater than/less than, skip counting, place value, even/odd numbers

## NCTM Curriculum Focal Points

**Number and Operations and Algebra:** Addition and subtraction strategies

**Number and Operations:** Whole number relationships, including grouping of tens and ones

## Number of Students

2–4 or entire class

## Materials

For each student:

- 20–40 Unifix Cubes
- Unifix 1–100 Board

For each group:

- Set of 1–100 Cards

## Getting Ready

Make a copy of the Unifix 1–100 Board for each student.

Give each student 20–40 Unifix Cubes.

Make copies of the 1–100 Cards and cut them apart. Depending on the activity being done, each group needs a set of cards.

## Digging In

Several bingo games focusing on different concepts or skills are possible using the Unifix 1–100 Board. The rules for each game are the same.

Taking turns, players draw a card from the deck, cover the appropriate number on the 1–100 Board with a Unifix Cube, and place the card in a discard pile.

The first player to get three, four, or five Unifix Cubes in a row, horizontally, vertically, or diagonally, is the winner.

### Game 1

Players cover the same number on the 1–100 Board as is shown on the card. Be sure to use an appropriate set of numbers based on the skill level of the students.

### Game 2

Remove the 100 card from the deck and add the 0 card. Players cover a number that is one more than the number on the card.

### Game 3

Players cover a number that is five more (or five less) than the number on the card. If a player draws 96 through 100 (or 1 through 5), he or she loses that turn.

### Game 4

Taking turns, players draw a number card. If it is an even (odd) number, players cover the corresponding even (odd) number on the 1–100 Board. If it is an odd (even) number, players lose a turn. The first player to get three even (odd) numbers in a row, horizontally or vertically, is the winner.

(Continued on next page)

# HUNDRED BOARD ACTIVITIES

## ➡ Going Further

Make a set of cards related to what is currently being taught. Read the cards to the entire class and have students cover the corresponding answers. Below are possible ideas for the cards.

- Count by 5s from 5 to 25
- Two 10s and three 1s (23)
- Numbers less than 44, ending in 4 (34, 24, 14, 4)
- Even numbers between 25 and 29
- Odd numbers between 34 and 40
- 1 less than 43
- 1 more than 37
- 10 more than 56

Mathematics with Unifix® Cubes          © Didax, Inc. – www.didax.com

# UNIFIX 1–100 BOARD

| 1 | 2 | 3 | 4 | 5 | 6 | 7 | 8 | 9 | 10 |
|---|---|---|---|---|---|---|---|---|---|
| 11 | 12 | 13 | 14 | 15 | 16 | 17 | 18 | 19 | 20 |
| 21 | 22 | 23 | 24 | 25 | 26 | 27 | 28 | 29 | 30 |
| 31 | 32 | 33 | 34 | 35 | 36 | 37 | 38 | 39 | 40 |
| 41 | 42 | 43 | 44 | 45 | 46 | 47 | 48 | 49 | 50 |
| 51 | 52 | 53 | 54 | 55 | 56 | 57 | 58 | 59 | 60 |
| 61 | 62 | 63 | 64 | 65 | 66 | 67 | 68 | 69 | 70 |
| 71 | 72 | 73 | 74 | 75 | 76 | 77 | 78 | 79 | 80 |
| 81 | 82 | 83 | 84 | 85 | 86 | 87 | 88 | 89 | 90 |
| 91 | 92 | 93 | 94 | 95 | 96 | 97 | 98 | 99 | 100 |

# HUNDRED BOARD ACTIVITIES

## 0–100 CARDS

| | | |
|---|---|---|
| 0 | 1 | 2 |
| 3 | 4 | 5 |
| 6 | 7 | 8 |
| 9 | 10 | 11 |
| 12 | 13 | 14 |
| 15 | 16 | 17 |

Mathematics with Unifix® Cubes        © Didax, Inc. – www.didax.com

# HUNDRED BOARD ACTIVITIES

## 0–100 CARDS

| | | |
|---|---|---|
| **18** | **19** | **20** |
| **21** | **22** | **23** |
| **24** | **25** | **26** |
| **27** | **28** | **29** |
| **30** | **31** | **32** |
| **33** | **34** | **35** |

## 0–100 CARDS

| | | |
|---|---|---|
| 36 | 37 | 38 |
| 39 | 40 | 41 |
| 42 | 43 | 44 |
| 45 | 46 | 47 |
| 48 | 49 | 50 |
| 51 | 52 | 53 |

Mathematics with Unifix® Cubes

# HUNDRED BOARD ACTIVITIES

## 0–100 CARDS

| | | |
|---|---|---|
| 54 | 55 | 56 |
| 57 | 58 | 59 |
| 60 | 61 | 62 |
| 63 | 64 | 65 |
| 66 | 67 | 68 |
| 69 | 70 | 71 |

## 0–100 CARDS

| | | |
|:---:|:---:|:---:|
| 72 | 73 | 74 |
| 75 | 76 | 77 |
| 78 | 79 | 80 |
| 81 | 82 | 83 |
| 84 | 85 | 86 |
| 87 | 88 | 89 |

Mathematics with Unifix® Cubes      © Didax, Inc. – www.didax.com

# HUNDRED BOARD ACTIVITIES

## 0–100 CARDS

| | | |
|---|---|---|
| **90** | **91** | **92** |
| **93** | **94** | **95** |
| **96** | **97** | **98** |
| **99** | **100** | **1 TO 100 CARDS** |
| | | |
| | | |

# WHAT COMES NEXT?

## Concept or Skills

Identify, describe, and extend color patterns

## NCTM Curriculum Focal Point

**Algebra Connection:** Identify, describe, and apply number patterns in developing strategies for basic facts

## Number of Students

1–entire class

## Materials

For each student:

- Several Unifix Cubes
- Several What Comes Next? Activity Sheet

For the teacher:

- Crayons or color stickers

## Getting Ready

Make several copies of the What Comes Next? Activity Sheet.

Using crayons or color stickers that are the same color as the Unifix Cubes, construct sheets with color patterns of varying levels of difficulty. For some, only two colors should be used.

Below are various patterns to use (X, O, #, and $ denote different colors of Unifix Cubes).

X O X O X O __ __ __ __ __ __

X O # $ X O # $ __ __ __ __

X X O O X X __ __ __ __ __ __

X X O # X __ __ # __ __ __ __

O X O O X __ __ __ __ __ __ __

X X O O # # # __ __ __ __ __

X O X __ X O X __ __ __ __ __

X O O # # # # __ __ __ __ __

X X X O O # __ __ __ __ __ __

X O __ O __ O X __ __ __ __ __

X O O # # # __ __ __ __ __ __

X X X O O # __ __ __ __ __ __

X O # X O # __ __ __ __ __ __

X X X O O O # __ __ __ __ __

X O # # # # __ __ __ __ __ __

X X O O O # $ X X __ __ __ __

## Digging In

Instruct students to cover each square in a row with the Unifix Cube of the corresponding color and to continue the pattern they observe. Ask students to describe in words the pattern created.

## Going Further

It is important to note that some students may continue color cube patterns in ways that are different than what is expected *and* describe their reasoning for the patterns logically and correctly. Asking students to explain their patterns is critical for mathematical communication.

Several of the examples of patterns provided allow for more than one correct answer by students. Discuss variations in patterns using particular examples.

After students have worked with several different What Comes Next? sheets, let them make their own patterns on a blank sheet. Shuffle the sheets and distribute them to other students to try.

# WHAT COMES NEXT?

# PATTERN MAKING

## Concept or Skills

Identify, describe, and extend color patterns denoted by symbols

## NCTM Curriculum Focal Point

**Algebra Connection:** Identify, describe, and apply number patterns in developing strategies for basic facts

## Number of Students

1–entire class

## Materials

For each student:

- Several Unifix Cubes
- Pattern-Making Mat
- Blank Pattern-Making Mat (optional)

## Getting Ready

Make several copies of the Pattern-Making Mat.

The ready-made mat has five rows of squares labeled with letters representing these Unifix Cube colors:

| | |
|---|---|
| R | Red |
| G | Green |
| Y | Yellow |
| O | Orange |
| W | White |
| BK | Black |

Or make your own patterns on the blank Pattern-Making Mat using these and other Unifix colors:

| | |
|---|---|
| BL | Blue |
| BR | Brown |
| LB | Light Blue |
| M | Maroon |

## Digging In

Instruct students to cover each square in a row with the Unifix Cube of the corresponding color and to continue the pattern they observe. Say:

- Look at the letter patterns on the sheet. Each letter represents a Unifix Cube color. What color does each of them represent?
- Cover each square with a Unifix Cube and continue the pattern.
- Tell me what color pattern you see.

## Going Further

It is important to note that some children may continue color cube patterns in ways that are different than what is expected *and* describe their reasoning for the patterns logically and correctly. Asking students to explain their patterns is critical for mathematical communication.

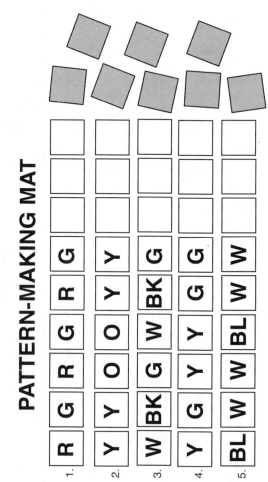

*Mathematics with Unifix® Cubes*     © Didax, Inc. – www.didax.com

Several of the examples of patterns provided allow for more than one correct answer by students. Here is an example of such a color pattern with possible descriptions of the pattern observed and the colors of three cubes added to the pattern:

RED, GREEN, RED, GREEN, GREEN, RED, GREEN, RED, …

Many students will see a repeating group of five as the pattern:

RGRGG

In this case, they would finish with **GGR**

RGRGG RGR**GG R**

Some students may look at the entire sequence of eight cubes:

RGRGGRGR

In this case, they would finish with RGR

RGRGGRGR **RGR**GGRGR

Some students may see groups of four cubes, with the colors alternating. In this case, they would finish with **RGR**.

RGRG GRGR **RGR**G

Some students may see a nonrepeating pattern of cubes:

RGRGG RGRGGG RGRGGGG

In this case, they would finish with **GGG**

RGRGG RGR**GGG**

Discuss variations in patterns for particular examples.

After students have worked through the Pattern-Making Mat, let them make their own letter patterns on a blank sheet. Shuffle the sheets and distribute them to other students to try.

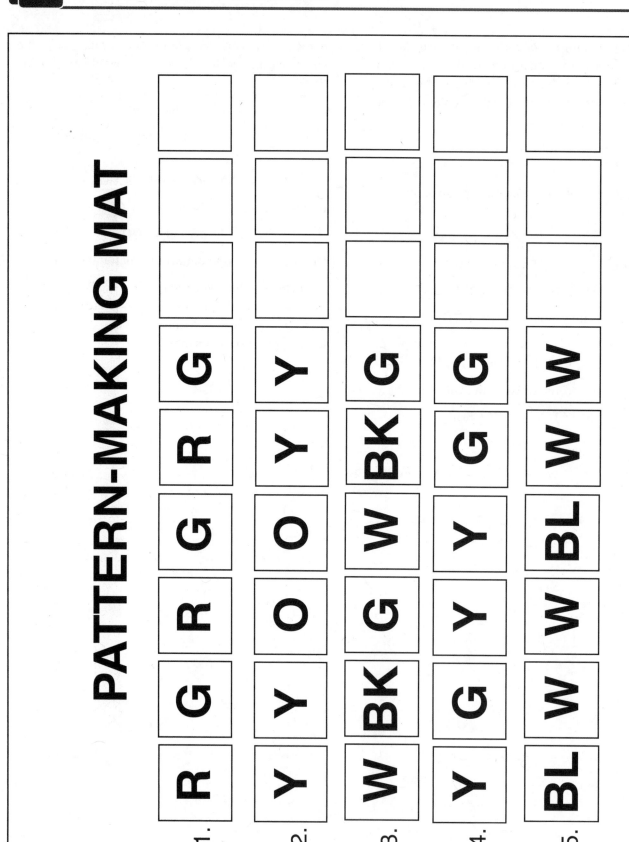

## PATTERN-MAKING MAT

| | | | | | |
|---|---|---|---|---|---|
| 1. | R | R | G | G | |
| 2. | Y | Y | O | Y | Y |
| 3. | W | BK | G | W | BK | G |
| 4. | Y | G | Y | G | G |
| 5. | BL | W | W | BL | W | W |

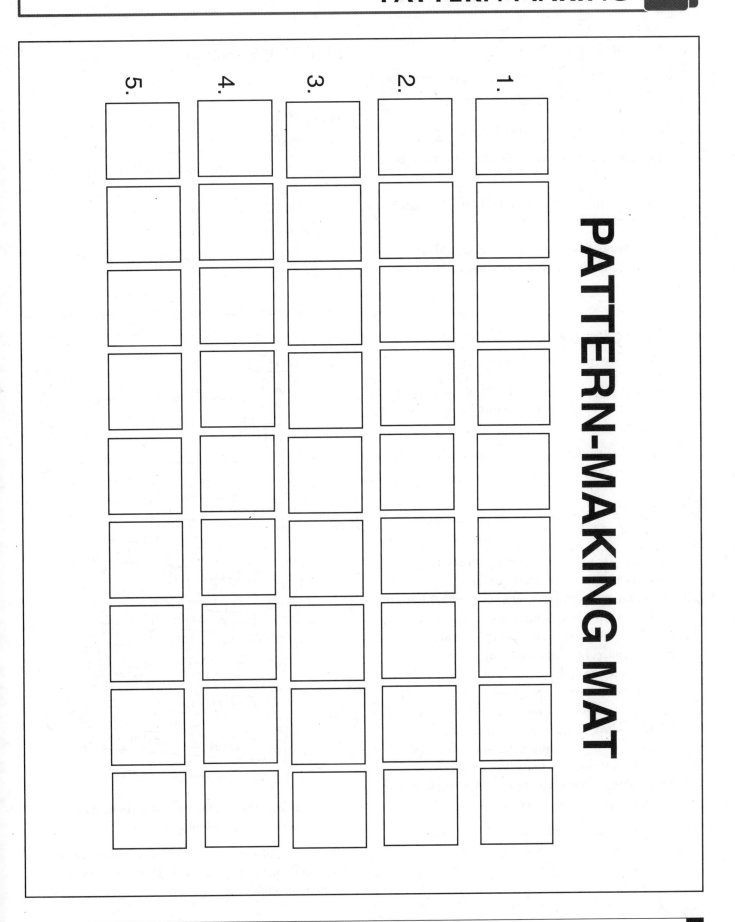

PATTERN-MAKING MAT

5.  4.  3.  2.  1.

# ARROW DIAGRAMS

## Concept or Skills

Logical reasoning skills, place value, algebraic reasoning, ordered pairs, graphing linear equations

## NCTM Curriculum Focal Point

**Number and Operations and Algebra:** Addition and subtraction strategies

**Number and Operations:** Whole number relationships, including grouping of tens and ones

**Algebra Connection:** Identify, describe, and apply number patterns in developing strategies for basic facts

## Number of Students

Entire class

## Materials

For each student:

- 5 Unifix Cubes of one color and 1 cube of a second color
- 0–99 Mat

For the class:

- Arrow Cards
- Blank Arrow Cards

## 🔷 Getting Ready

Make a copy of the 0–99 Mat for each student.

Make copies of the Arrow Cards and cut them apart. If the blank cards are used, write a number in the starting number square.

Distribute five Unifix Cubes of one color and one cube of a different color to each student.

## 🔷 Digging In

Discuss with students how arrow diagrams work. Say:

- **I am going to give you a starting number.**
- **Place a Unifix Cube on that number.**
- **Then I am going to give you a series of arrows. For each arrow, place a Unifix Cube.**
- **Use the same cube color until the last arrow. Then change colors on that arrow (the answer).**
- **An arrow to the right → means move one place to the right of the last number and place a cube.**
- **An arrow to the left ← means move one place to the left of the last number and place a cube.**
- **An arrow down ↓ means move one place down from the last number and place a cube.**
- **An arrow up ↑ means move one place up from the last number and place a cube.**

Present an example, such as the following, on the chalkboard or overhead for students to follow.

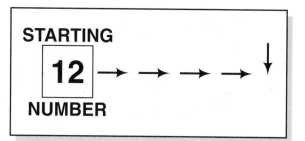

After working through the example, present other arrow diagrams for students to solve.

If desired, make transparencies of the Arrow cards and cut them apart. Place a card on the overhead for students to solve.

# ARROW DIAGRAMS

## Going Further

After working through several different arrow diagrams, discuss the mathematics involved.

- An arrow to the right adds 1 to the previous number.
- An arrow to the left subtracts 1 from the previous number.
- An arrow down adds 10 to the previous number.
- An arrow up subtracts 10 from the previous number.
- Therefore, the net result of an arrow to the right *and* an arrow to the left is 0 (1 − 1 = 0).
- The net result of an arrow down and an arrow up is 0 (10 − 10 = 0).

Ask the students:

- Can you tell me what each arrow does to the last number? What does an arrow to the right do?
- What does an arrow to the left do?
- What does an arrow down do?
- What does an arrow up do?

A pair of arrows in opposite directions is called a **zero pair**, which becomes a major idea later for algebra.

On the chalkboard or overhead, present different starting numbers for the same set of arrows. Have students find the resulting number. Here is an example:

$$12 \rightarrow\rightarrow\downarrow\downarrow\leftarrow 33$$
$$40 \rightarrow\rightarrow\downarrow\downarrow\leftarrow 61$$
$$73 \rightarrow\rightarrow\downarrow\downarrow\leftarrow 94$$
$$35 \rightarrow\rightarrow\downarrow\downarrow\leftarrow 56$$
$$0 \rightarrow\rightarrow\downarrow\downarrow\leftarrow 21$$

Discuss the pattern that occurs. In this example, the "rule" is "add 21." The above activity leads to ordered pairs of numbers, which show a linear relationship that can be graphed in a coordinate plane.

| Start | End |
|-------|-----|
| 12    | 33  |
| 40    | 61  |
| 73    | 94  |
| 35    | 56  |
| 0     | 21  |

Show and discuss with students that the order in which arrows are calculated does not matter. For the example above, $\rightarrow\rightarrow\downarrow\downarrow\leftarrow$ is the same as $\rightarrow\rightarrow\leftarrow\downarrow\downarrow$, which is the same as $\downarrow\downarrow\rightarrow\rightarrow\leftarrow$.

## 0–99 MAT

| 0 | 1 | 2 | 3 | 4 | 5 | 6 | 7 | 8 | 9 |
|---|---|---|---|---|---|---|---|---|---|
| 10 | 11 | 12 | 13 | 14 | 15 | 16 | 17 | 18 | 19 |
| 20 | 21 | 22 | 23 | 24 | 25 | 26 | 27 | 28 | 29 |
| 30 | 31 | 32 | 33 | 34 | 35 | 36 | 37 | 38 | 39 |
| 40 | 41 | 42 | 43 | 44 | 45 | 46 | 47 | 48 | 49 |
| 50 | 51 | 52 | 53 | 54 | 55 | 56 | 57 | 58 | 59 |
| 60 | 61 | 62 | 63 | 64 | 65 | 66 | 67 | 68 | 69 |
| 70 | 71 | 72 | 73 | 74 | 75 | 76 | 77 | 78 | 79 |
| 80 | 81 | 82 | 83 | 84 | 85 | 86 | 87 | 88 | 89 |
| 90 | 91 | 92 | 93 | 94 | 95 | 96 | 97 | 98 | 99 |

# ARROW CARDS

**STARTING**
**30**
→ → → ↑ ←
**NUMBER**

**STARTING**
**74**
← ↑ ← ↑ ↑
**NUMBER**

**STARTING**
**44**
→ → ↓ ↓ →
**NUMBER**

**STARTING**
**29**
→ → ↓ ↓ ↓
**NUMBER**

**STARTING**
**63**
← ← ↑ ← ↑
**NUMBER**

**STARTING**
**45**
← ← ↓ → ↓
**NUMBER**

**STARTING**
**58**
← ↓ ↓ → →
**NUMBER**

**STARTING**
**87**
→ → ↑ ↑ ←
**NUMBER**

# ARROW DIAGRAMS

# ARROW CARDS

| | |
|---|---|
| **STARTING** [ ] → → → ↑ ← **NUMBER** | **STARTING** [ ] ← ↑ ← ↑ ↑ **NUMBER** |
| **STARTING** [ ] → → ↓ ↓ → **NUMBER** | **STARTING** [ ] → ↓ → ↓ ↓ **NUMBER** |
| **STARTING** [ ] ← ← ↑ ← ↑ **NUMBER** | **STARTING** [ ] ← ← ↓ → ↓ **NUMBER** |
| **STARTING** [ ] ← ↓ ↓ → → **NUMBER** | **STARTING** [ ] → → ↑ ↑ ← **NUMBER** |

Mathematics with Unifix® Cubes

## Concept or Skills

Counting, greater than/less than (more/less), perimeter, area

## NCTM Curriculum Focal Points

**Number and Operations:** Whole number relationships, including grouping of tens and ones

**Measurement and Data Analysis Connection:** Solve problems involving measurements and data

## Number of Students

1, small group, or entire class

## Materials

For each student:

- 20 Unifix Cubes
- Set of Cube Count Cards
- 1 Cube Count Record Sheet

---

## 1 Getting Ready

Make copies of the Cube Count Cards and cut them apart. Make a copy of the Cube Count Record Sheet for each student.

Distribute 20 Unifix Cubes and a record sheet to each student.

## 2 Digging In

Instruct students to cover each outlined area on a card with Unifix Cubes, to count the number of cubes used, and to write the number in the blank by the appropriate card number on the record sheet.

Pose questions such as the following:

- Which figure is covered with the most Unifix Cubes?
- Which figure is covered with the fewest Unifix Cubes?
- Are any figures covered with the same number of Unifix Cubes?
- For a given figure, did anyone have a different number of cubes?

## 3 Going Further

Use the blank Cube Count Cards to create new figures to cover.

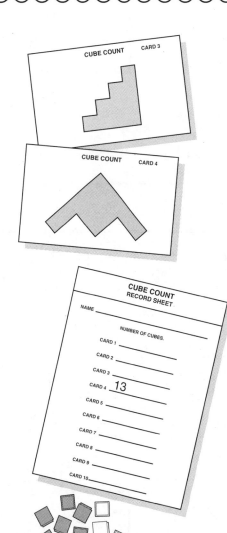

## CUBE COUNT — CARD 1

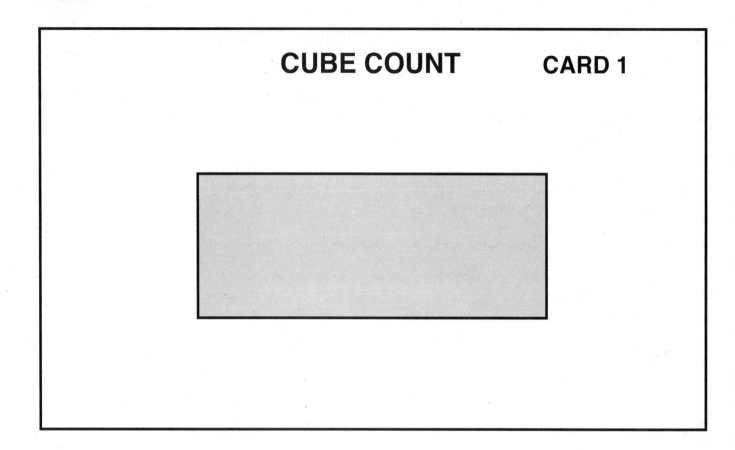

## CUBE COUNT — CARD 2

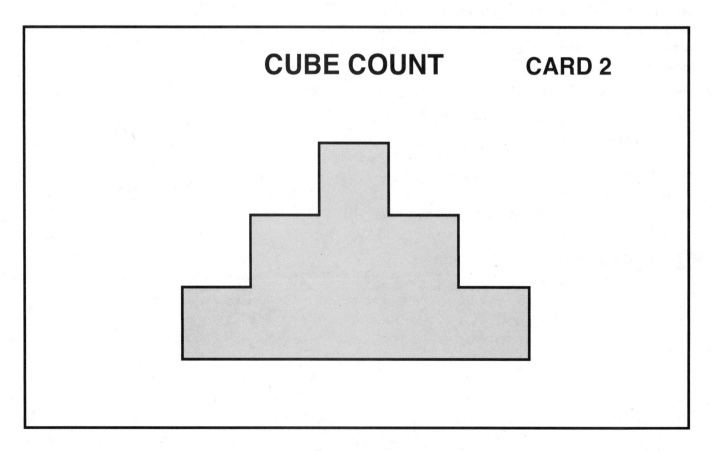

## CUBE COUNT          CARD 3

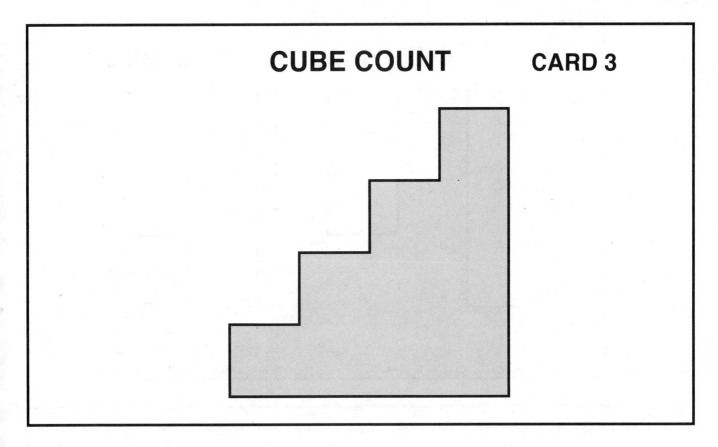

## CUBE COUNT          CARD 4

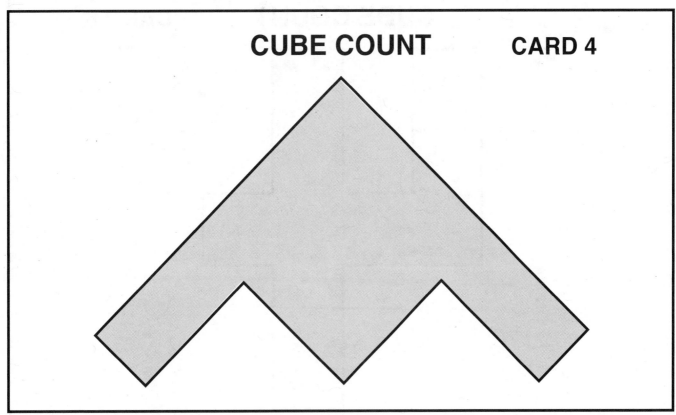

## CUBE COUNT    CARD 5

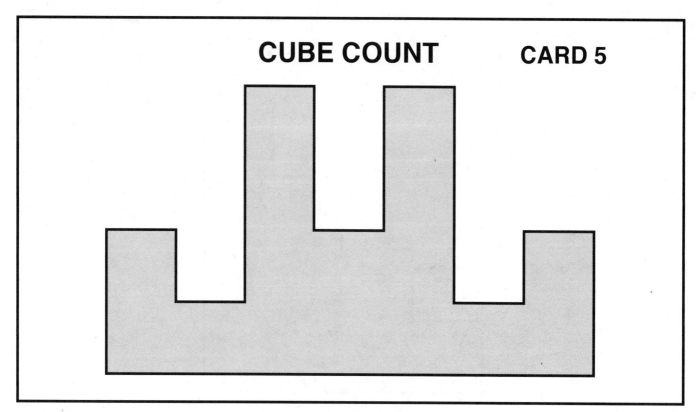

## CUBE COUNT    CARD 6

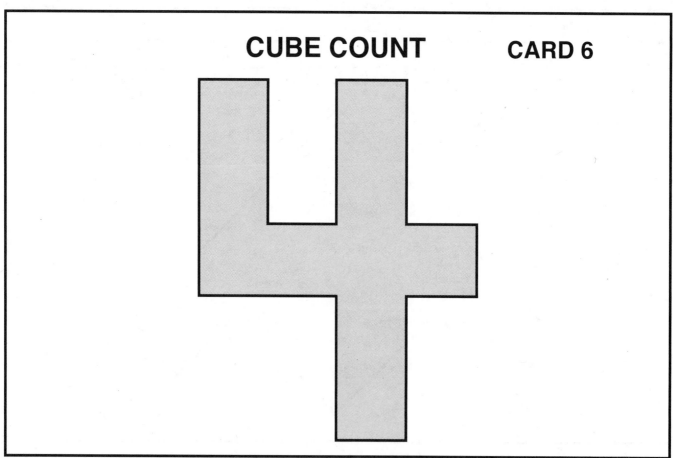

Mathematics with Unifix® Cubes    © Didax, Inc. – www.didax.com

# CUBE COUNT        CARD 7

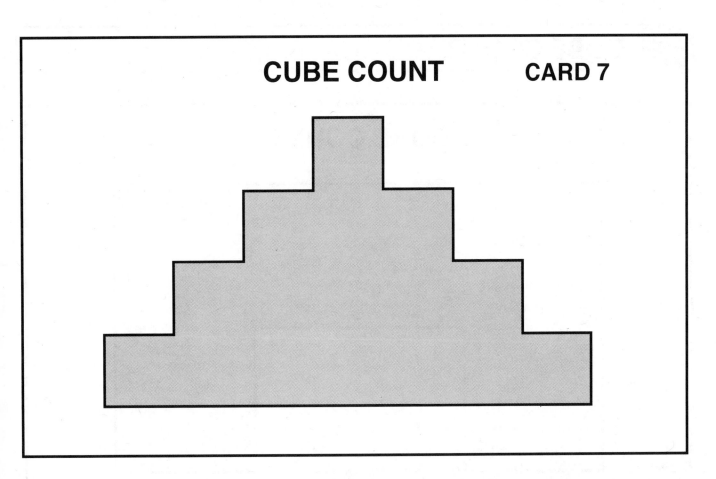

# CUBE COUNT        CARD 8

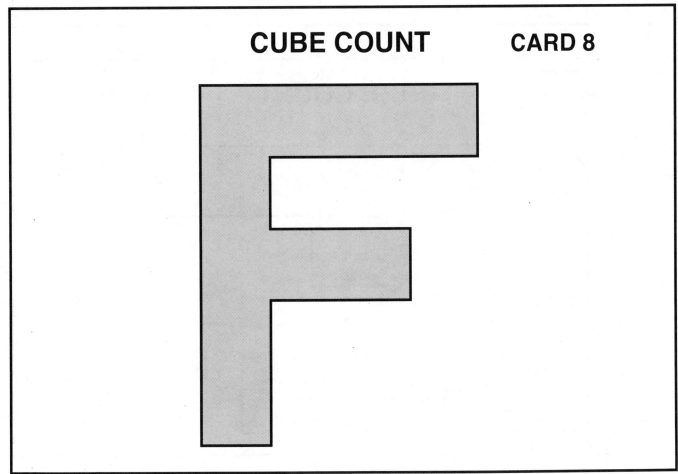

## CUBE COUNT          CARD 9

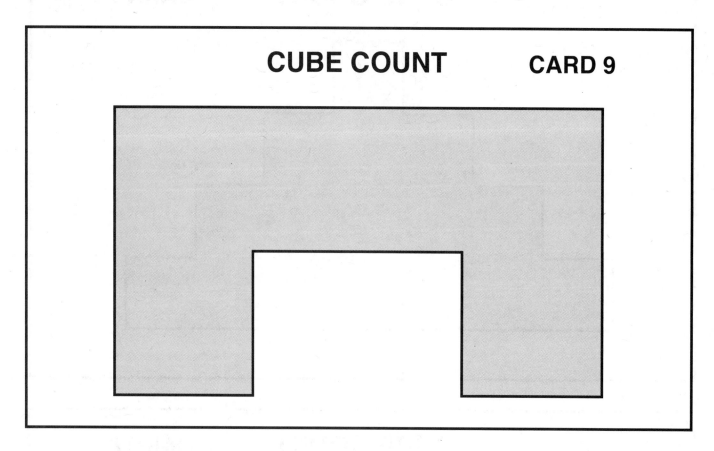

## CUBE COUNT          CARD 10

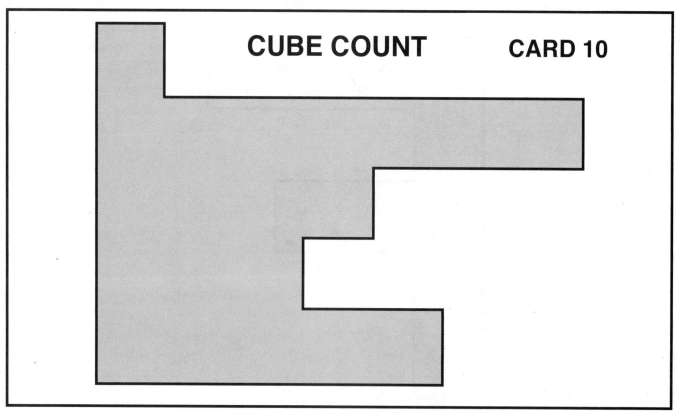

**CUBE COUNT**                    CARD _____

**CUBE COUNT**                    CARD _____

## CUBE COUNT
### RECORD SHEET

NAME _____

### NUMBER OF CUBES

CARD 1 _____

CARD 2 _____

CARD 3 _____

CARD 4 _____

CARD 5 _____

CARD 6 _____

CARD 7 _____

CARD 8 _____

CARD 9 _____

CARD _____

Mathematics with Unifix® Cubes © Didax, Inc. – www.didax.com

# PERFECT PLACEMENT

## Concept or Skills

Spatial terms (above/below, left/right, on, next to, beside)

## NCTM Curriculum Focal Point

**Geometry:** Composing and decomposing geometric shapes

## Number of Students

Small group or entire class

## Materials

For each student:

- 10 Unifix Cubes (one of each color)
- Perfect Placement Mat 1 or 2

For each group:

- Perfect Placement cards (optional)

## Getting Ready

Make a copy of the appropriate Perfect Placement Mat for each student. Give each student a mat and 10 Unifix Cubes.

## Digging In

This activity focuses on visual/spatial sense terminology. There are two Perfect Placement mats for students to use. Mat 1 shows a single line dividing the mat, with no squares on the mat. Mat 2 shows squares in various locations.

### Mat 1

Instruct students to arrange their Perfect Placement Mat 1 horizontally or vertically, depending on the terminology being discussed.

Teacher directions such as the following can be presented:

- Place a red Unifix Cube above (below) the line.
- Place two yellow Unifix Cubes above (below) the line.
- Place a blue Unifix Cube on the line.
- Place a green Unifix Cube above the line and a white Unifix Cube below the line.
- Place three brown Unifix Cubes above the line and four black Unifix Cubes below the line.
- Place an orange Unifix Cube at the right (left) end of the line.
- Place a white Unifix Cube in the upper (lower) right (left) hand corner.

- Place a brown Unifix Cube on the right (left) side of the line.
- Place a light blue Unifix Cube on the middle of the line.
- Place a dark blue Unifix Cube beside the line.
- Place a white Unifix Cube between the (red) Unifix Cube and the (black) Unifix Cube.
- Place a brown Unifix Cube on top of the yellow Unifix Cube.
- Place a red Unifix Cube at the top (bottom) of the mat.

### Mat 2

Instruct students to arrange their Perfect Placement Mat 2 horizontally or vertically, depending on the terminology being discussed.

Since squares are shown on Mat 2, specific directions about location can be presented. If the line is vertical, then here are the locations shown:

- Upper left-hand corner
- Upper right-hand corner
- Top of line
- Bottom of line
- Lower right-hand corner
- Lower left-hand corner
- Left side of line
- Right side of line
- Middle of line
- Beside the line

(Continued on next page)

# PERFECT PLACEMENT

## ➡ Going Further

For individual practice, distribute the Perfect Placement cards to each group. Instruct students to draw a card from the deck and place a Unifix Cube of the designated color in the appropriate location.

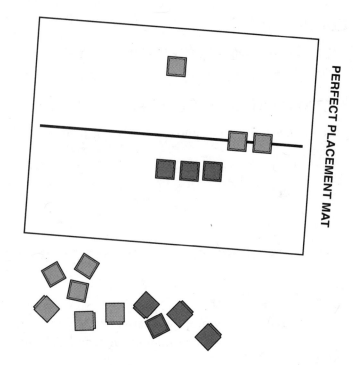

PERFECT PLACEMENT MAT

Mathematics with Unifix® Cubes

# PERFECT PLACEMENT MAT 1

# PERFECT PLACEMENT MAT 2

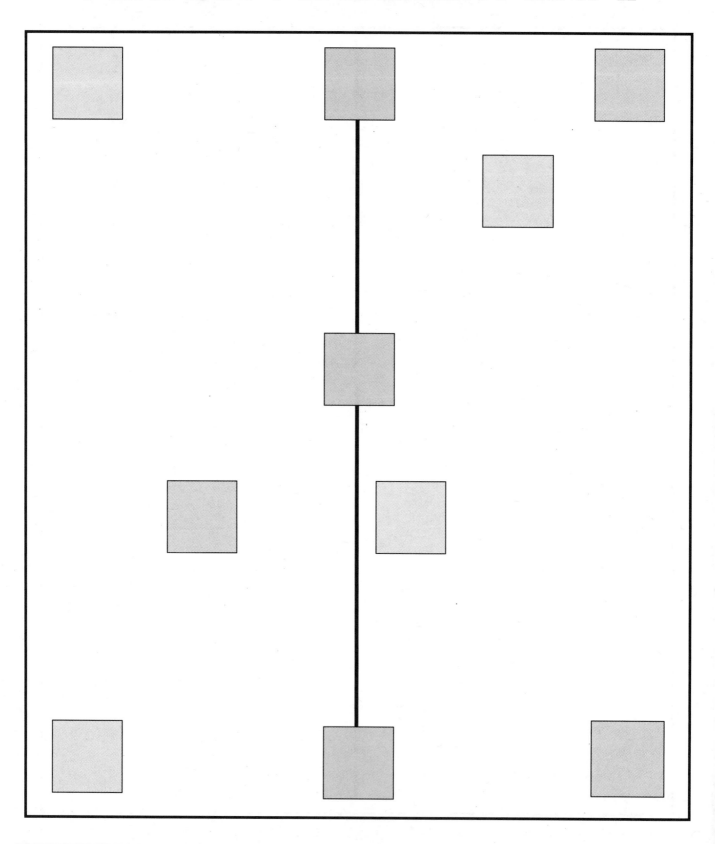

Mathematics with Unifix® Cubes
© Didax, Inc. – www.didax.com

# PERFECT PLACEMENT CARDS

| | | |
|---|---|---|
| Place a red Unifix Cube at the right end of the line. | Place a yellow Unifix Cube at the left end of the line. | Place a green Unifix Cube in the upper right-hand corner. |
| Place a dark blue Unifix Cube in the lower right-hand corner. | Place a brown Unifix Cube in the upper left-hand corner. | Place a black Unifix Cube in the lower left-hand corner. |
| Place an orange Unifix Cube next to the line. | Place a white Unifix Cube above the line. | Place a light blue Unifix Cube below the line. |
| Place a maroon Unifix Cube on the right side of the line. | Place a red Unifix Cube on the left side of the line. | Place a yellow Unifix Cube in the middle of the line. |
| Place a green Unifix Cube on top of the line. | Place a dark blue Unifix Cube beside the line. | Place a brown Unifix Cube at the top of the mat. |
| Place a light blue Unifix Cube at the bottom of the mat. | Place a black Unifix Cube between the green and dark blue Unifix Cubes. | Place an orange Unifix Cube on top of the white Unifix Cube. |

# HOW LONG IS YOUR FOOT?

## Concept or Skills

Estimating length, measuring length, graphing data

## NCTM Curriculum Focal Point

**Measurement and Data Analysis Connection:** Solve problems involving measurements and data; measure using groups of tens and ones; represent measurements and data in picture and bar graphs

## Number of Students

Entire class

## Materials

For each student:

- 10–12 Unifix Cubes
- Unifix Cube Grid Sheet (optional)

## 🕐 Getting Ready

Make a copy of the Unifix Cube Grid Sheet for each student. Give each student 10–12 Unifix Cubes and a grid sheet.

## 🔧 Digging In

Have students estimate the length of their feet in Unifix Cubes. Decide if shoes are on or off.

Say:

**I want you to estimate the length of your foot in Unifix Cubes. You can look at your foot and look at the Unifix Cubes, but you cannot place cubes next to your foot to find out the length.**

**Write your estimate on a piece of paper, and then use the Unifix Cubes to measure your foot.**

For some students, it may be easier to work in pairs using the grid sheet. One student places his or her foot on the sheet, aligning the heel with one of the horizontal lines. The other student marks the tip of the toe, and together they determine the number of cubes needed by placing them in a line on the sheet.

Pose questions such as the following:

- Who has the longest (shortest) foot?
- How many have a foot that is (number) cubes in length?
- What foot length is the most common?

The last question leads to a discussion of the statistical term **mode**, the score in a data set that occurs most frequently. Young children easily understand the concept, regardless of whether the vocabulary is introduced.

Discussing foot lengths also leads to simple graphing activities with Unifix Cubes using the grid sheet. Construct a class frequency graph foot lengths.

Assign particular Unifix Cube colors to foot sizes. For example, red will be length 5, green will be length 6, and so on.

Have students create vertical or horizontal bar graphs with their cubes, shading the number of squares corresponding to frequencies, as shown below.

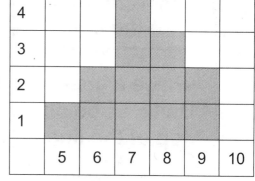

**Foot Length in Cubes**

For vertical bar graphs, the foot length that has the tallest bar represents the mode. For horizontal bar graphs, the foot length that has the longest bar represents the mode.

## Going Further

Repeat the previous activity by having students estimate and measure their hand spans from the end of their little finger to the end of their thumb.

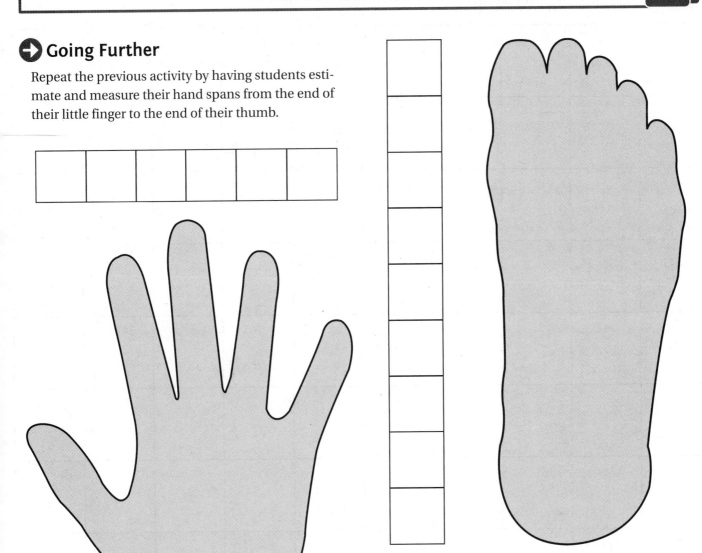

# UNIFIX CUBE GRID SHEET

Mathematics with Unifix® Cubes

© Didax, Inc. – www.didax.com

# MAKING BAR GRAPHS

## Concept or Skills

Constructing and interpreting horizontal and vertical bar graphs

## NCTM Curriculum Focal Point

**Measurement and Data Analysis Connection:** Solve problems involving measurements and data; represent measurements and data in picture and bar graphs

## Number of Students

2–3

## Materials

For each student:

- 40 Unifix Cubes (10 each in four colors – red, white, green, black)
- Making Bar Graphs Grid Sheet (colors designated)
- Making Bar Graphs Grid Sheet (no colors designated)—optional

For each group:

- Making Bar Graphs Spinner Sheet (colors designated)
- Making Bar Graphs Spinner Sheet (no colors designated)—optional
- Spinner

## Getting Ready

Make a copy of the desired grid sheet (with or without colors) for each student.

Make a copy of the corresponding spinner sheet for each group. If the blank sheet is used, write four different colors of Unifix Cubes in the appropriate locations on the sheet.

## Digging In

The spinner sheet is designed to provide an ordered pair (color, number of cubes).

Taking turns, students spin the spinner and take the corresponding color and number of Unifix Cubes. They place the cubes in the corresponding column of their Making Bar Graphs grid sheet.

Play continues in the same manner until one student completely fills a column with cubes of the same color. A column does not need to be filled with exactly 10 cubes. For example, a student may have a column with 8 red cubes, and then spin 4 red, which now fills the column.

After students have completed a game, ask questions about their graphs such as the following:

- Which of the bars on your graph have the greatest number of cubes? Least?

- Are there any bars on your graph that have an equal number of cubes?
- What is the total number of cubes on your bar graph?

If an entire class is participating, record class data on the board and discuss the results.

## Going Further

A blank spinner sheet and grid are provided so that any four Unifix colors can be used.

**SPINNER SHEET**

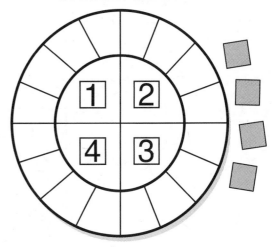

# MAKING BAR GRAPHS

## GRID SHEET

| | | | |
|---|---|---|---|
| | | | |
| | | | |
| | | | |
| | | | |
| | | | |
| | | | |
| | | | |
| | | | |
| | | | |
| RED | WHITE | GREEN | BLACK |

FREQUENCY

Mathematics with Unifix® Cubes          © Didax, Inc. – www.didax.com

## GRID SHEET

**FREQUENCY**

# SPINNER SHEET

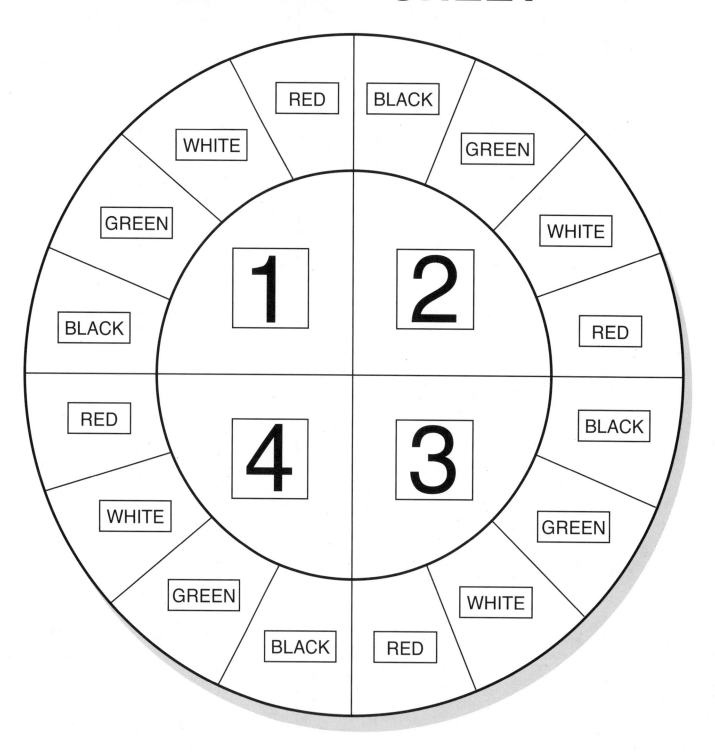

Mathematics with Unifix® Cubes                    © Didax, Inc. – www.didax.com

# SPINNER SHEET

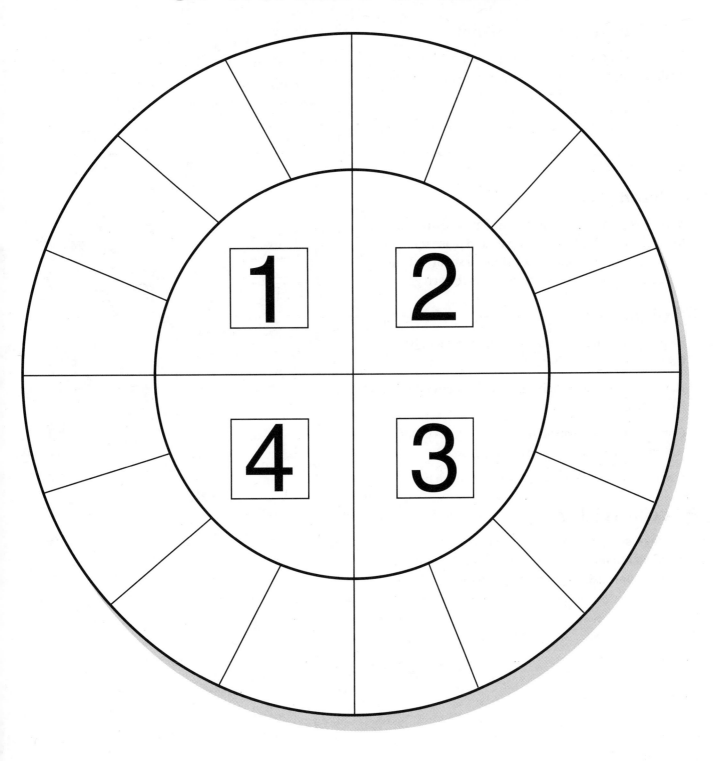

Mathematics with Unifix® Cubes

# LINE UP

## Concept or Skills

Ordering by length

## NCTM Curriculum Focal Point

**Measurement and Data Analysis Connection:** Solve problems involving measurements and data; measure using groups of tens and ones; represent measurements and data in picture and bar graphs

## Number of Students

1–3

## Materials

For each group:

- 55 Unifix Cubes
- Measurement Bars Activity Sheet

## Getting Ready

Make a copy of the Measurement Bars activity sheet for each group. Cut the bars apart and place them in plastic bags or envelopes. Distribute a set of 55 Unifix Cubes and a set of Measurement Bars to each group.

## Digging In

Instruct students to remove the Measurement Bars from the envelope or bag and divide them up.

Have students cover each bar with a structured bar of Unifix Cubes.

Once this task is finished, have the students order the structured bars from shortest to longest.

Discuss how many Unifix Cubes are in each bar.

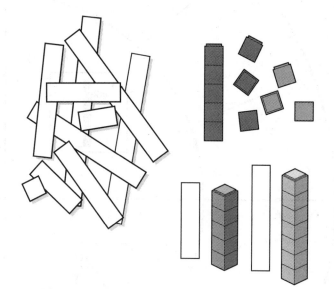

## Going Further

Use legal size paper to make Measurement Bars that are longer than 10 Unifix Cubes in length. Unifix Cubes measure approximately 2 cm × 2 cm (or ¾" × ¾").

# MEASUREMENT BARS

# UNIFIX BINGO

## Concept or Skills

Color recognition or discrimination, number recognition

## NCTM Curriculum Focal Point

**Measurement and Data Analysis Connection:** Solve problems involving measurements and data; represent measurements and data in picture and bar graphs

## Number of Students

Small group or entire class

## Materials

- 20 Unifix Cubes (two each of all 10 colors) for each student, plus an identical set in a bag to use for drawing
- Unifix Bingo Card for each student
- Color stickers for each cube color, or crayons or marking pens corresponding to the Unifix colors

## Getting Ready

Make a classroom set of Unifix Bingo Cards using card stock. Either color the cards with crayons or use color stickers corresponding to the Unifix Cube colors. Since there are 16 squares on a card and only 10 Unifix Cube colors, use six of the 10 colors twice to complete the card, or select eight colors and use each color twice to complete the card.

Prepare a paper bag containing 20 Unifix Cubes (two each of 10 colors, or two each of 8 colors if only 8 colors are used).

## Digging In

The teacher or a designated student draws a Unifix Cube from the bag of 20 and shows it to the other students.

Each student covers *one* square of that color on his or her bingo card with a Unifix Cube of the same color.

The first student to cover four squares in a row, horizontally, vertically, or diagonally, or in the four corners, is the winner.

To make the game go faster, let students cover all squares of a particular color.

## Going Further

Make a classroom set of Unifix Bingo Cards, using the digits 0 through 9 on each card. Similar to the cards with colors, duplicates of six digits will be needed.

Make a set of caller cards with each of the numbers on a card, two of each number 0 through 9.

Play Unifix Bingo as indicated above, using Unifix Cubes to cover the numbers.

Mathematics with Unifix® Cubes

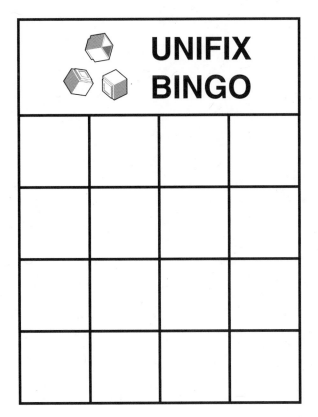

UNIFIX
BINGO

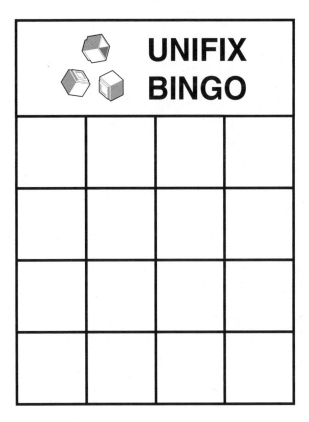

UNIFIX
BINGO

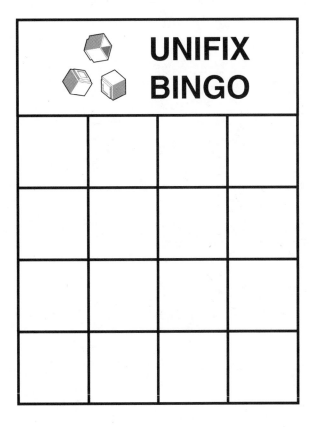

UNIFIX
BINGO

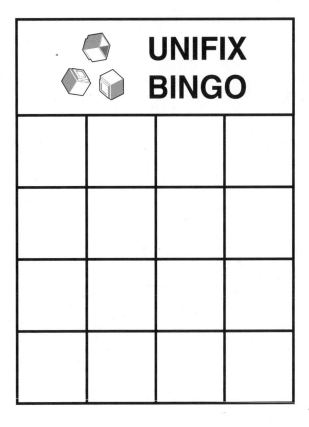

UNIFIX
BINGO

# SPINNER SHEETS
## 1–10
## 0–9
## 2–11

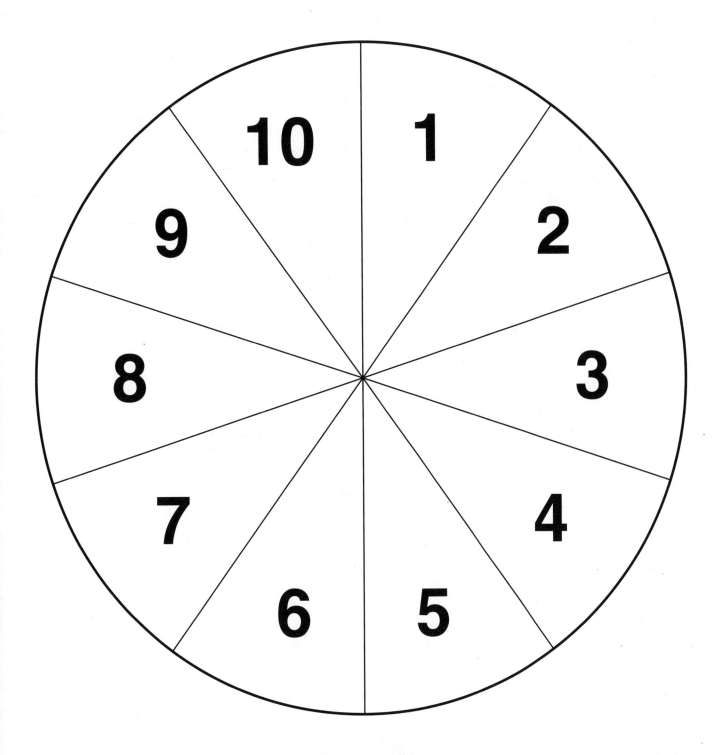

# 1–10
# SPINNER SHEET

Mathematics with Unifix® Cubes

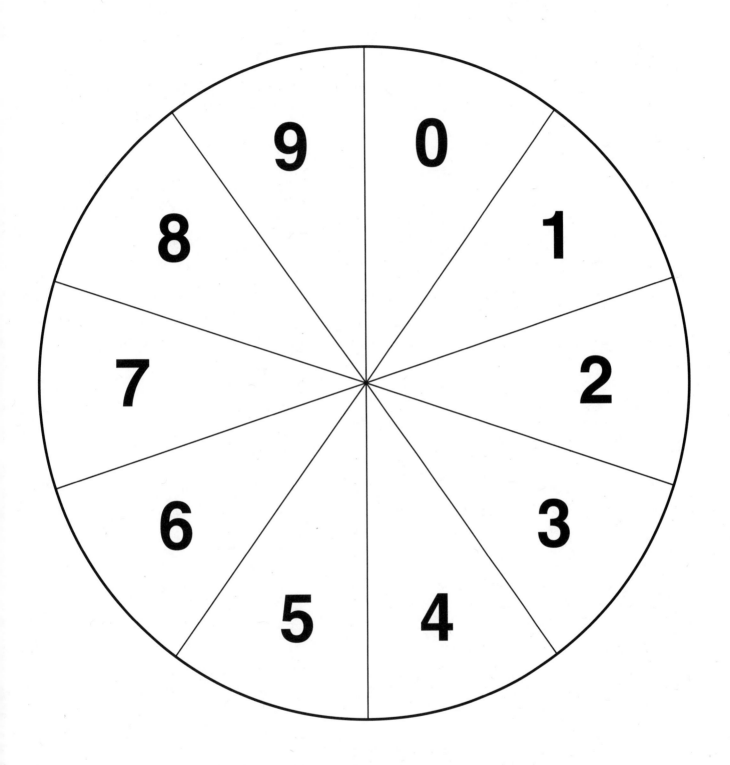

# 0–9
# SPINNER SHEET

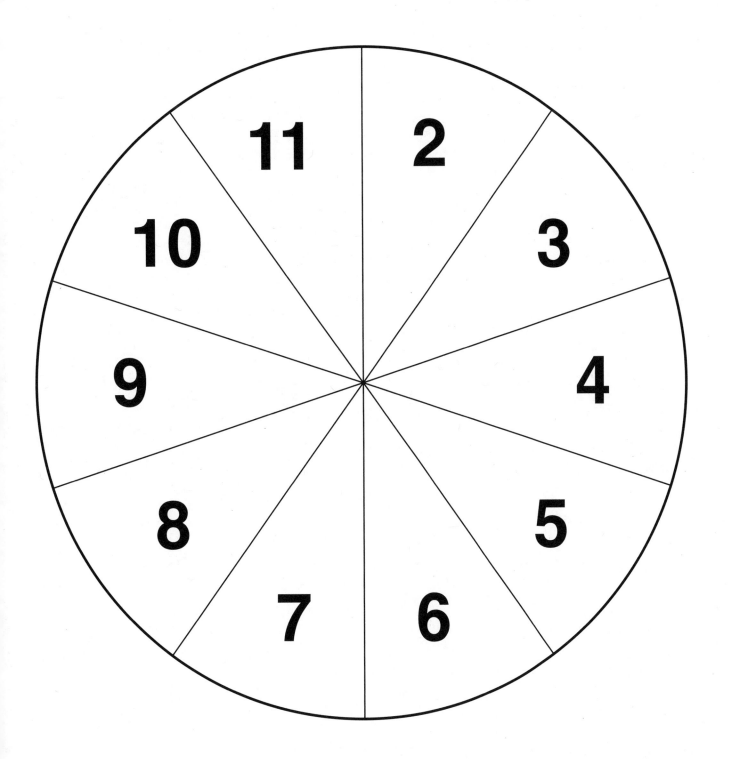

## 2–11
## SPINNER SHEET

Mathematics with Unifix® Cubes